# Basic Current Procedural Terminology and HCPCS Coding Exercises

## Fourth Edition

### Gail I. Smith, MA, RHIA, CCS-P

AHIMA PRESS

ISBN: 978-1-58426-461-3

AHIMA Product Number AC210615

Caitlin Wilson, Assistant Editor

Ashley R. Latta, Production Development Editor

Pamela Woolf, Director of Publications

All information contained within this book, including websites and regulatory information, was current and valid as of the date of publication. However, webpage addresses and the information on them may change or disappear at any time and for any number of reasons. The user is encouraged to perform his or her own general web searches to locate any site addresses listed here that are no longer valid.

Please contact publications@ahima.org to notify us of any potential inaccuracies in this text.

American Health Information Management Association
233 North Michigan Avenue, 21st Floor
Chicago, Illinois 60601-5809
ahima.org

# Contents

# About the Author

Gail I. Smith, MA, RHIA, CCS-P, is president of Gail I. Smith Consulting in Cincinnati, Ohio, and has over 35 years experience in the field of coding, education, and health information management (HIM). Ms. Smith was an associate professor and a director of the health information management program at the University of Cincinnati in Cincinnati, Ohio. Prior to joining the faculty at the University of Cincinnati, she was a director of a health information technology program and was health information manager in a multihospital healthcare system.

Ms. Smith also is a coding consultant and a frequent presenter at conferences throughout the United States. An active member of the American Health Information Management Association (AHIMA), she has served on the board of directors and several of AHIMA's committees and task forces.

Ms. Smith received a Bachelor of Science degree in health information management from the Ohio State University in Columbus, Ohio, and a Master of Arts degree in education from the College of Mt. St. Joseph in Cincinnati.

# Acknowledgments

The author wishes to thank her husband, Mark, and daughter, Kristin, for their constant support.

---

AHIMA Press would like to thank Tina L. Cressman, CCS, CCS-P, CPC, CPC-H, CPC-P, CEMC for her review and feedback on this book.

# Preface

This workbook serves as a companion to *Basic Current Procedural Terminology and HCPCS Coding* published by the American Health Information Management Association (AHIMA). It is designed to provide additional practice exercises for applying CPT coding guidelines to case studies. In addition, medical terminology is reinforced with matching quizzes, questions reinforcing medical terminology and clinical concepts, and crossword puzzles.

## Organization of the Workbook

The workbook follows the same chapter titles as *Basic Current Procedural Terminology and HCPCS Coding*. Students are asked to identify the key terms for locating the coding selection (code or range of codes to verify), answer documentation questions, and assign index terms and CPT codes to describe the procedures and services. Actual case studies and operative reports provide an opportunity for students to analyze documentation to support accurate coding selection. The partial answer key presented in Appendix A offers answers to all terminology and clinical concept questions as well as some answers and rationales for coding drills and case studies. The complete answer key is only available to approved instructors. The author's explanations of the correct answers provide a better understanding of the relationship between documentation and correct assignment of CPT code(s). The following is a summary of chapter highlights:

| Chapter | Title | Activities |
|---------|-------|------------|
| 1 | Introduction to Clinical Coding | Self-Assessment<br>Crossword Puzzle |
| 2 | Application of the CPT System | Matching Exercise<br>Referencing CPT Assistant<br>Application of CPT Exercises |
| 3 | Modifiers | Matching Exercise<br>Select Modifier Exercises<br>Coding/Modifier Case Studies |

| Chapter | Title | Activities |
|---------|-------|------------|
| 4 | Surgery | Medical Terminology Review<br>Crossword Puzzles<br>Clinical Concepts Exercises<br>Coding Drills<br>Operative Notes<br>Emergency Department Records<br>Operative Reports<br>Physician Office Records |
| 5 | Radiology | Medical Terminology Review<br>Case Studies |
| 6 | Pathology and Laboratory Services | Case Studies |
| 7 | Evaluation and Management Services | Case Studies |
| 8 | Medicine | Case Studies |
| 9 | Anesthesia | Case Studies |
| 10 | HCPCS Level II | Case Studies |
| 11 | Reimbursement in the Ambulatory Setting | Crossword Puzzle<br>Case Studies |
| | Appendix A | Odd-numbered Answer Key |

# Chapter 1

# Introduction to Clinical Coding

Chapter 1 provides an overview of coding and its use in the claims submission process. It is vital that the CPT codes and ICD-10-CM codes provided are supported by the documentation in the patient's medical record. The ICD-10-CM diagnosis code should identify *why* the patient was seeking services (treatment, therapy, and so on), and CPT codes should identify the services that were performed.

In the following case studies, identify the CPT code that would support the ICD-10-CM diagnosis code.

## Exercise 1.1: CPT Code Selection

In the following multiple-choice questions, identify the most appropriate CPT code that would be linked to the ICD-10-CM diagnosis code.

1. Patient presents with a 1.0 cm carbuncle on the posterior section of the neck. The surgeon performs an incision and drainage of the carbuncle.

   ICD-10-CM code: L02.13 Carbuncle of neck

   Which of the following CPT codes would be linked to this diagnosis?

   a. 10060 Incision and drainage of abscess (such as carbuncle, suppurative hidradenitis, cutaneous or subcutaneous abscess, cyst, furuncle, or paronychia); simple or single
   b. 20005 Incision and drainage of soft tissue abscess, subfascial (ie, involves the soft tissue below the deep fascia)
   c. 21550 Biopsy, soft tissue of neck or thorax
   d. 21555 Excision, tumor, soft tissue of neck or anterior thorax, subcutaneous; less than 3 cm

2. The 3-year-old child was seen in the pediatrician's office after placing a pebble in his left nostril. The physician removed the pebble without difficulty.

   ICD-10-CM code: T17.1XXA Foreign body in nostril

   Which of the following CPT codes would be linked to this diagnosis?

   a. 30110 Excision, nasal polyp(s); simple
   b. 30150 Rhinectomy; partial

   c.   30300 Removal of foreign body, intranasal; office type of procedure
   d.   30310 Removal of foreign body, intranasal; requiring general anesthesia

3.  The 55-year-old male patient had multiple ureteral strictures that were surgically treated with balloon dilation via cystoureteroscopy.

   ICD-10-CM code: N13.5 Crossing vessel and stricture of ureter without hydronephrosis

   Which of the following CPT codes would be linked to this diagnosis?

   a.   52000 Cystourethroscopy (separate procedure)
   b.   52275 Cystourethroscopy, with internal urethrotomy; male
   c.   52341 Cystourethroscopy, with treatment of ureteral stricture (such as balloon dilation, laser, electrocautery, and incision)
   d.   52344 Cystourethroscopy, with ureteroscopy; with treatment of ureteral stricture (eg. balloon dilation, laser, electrocautery, and incision)

4.  The patient is seeking medical treatment for dysphagia. ICD-10-CM code: R13.10 Dysphagia

   Which of the following CPT codes would be linked to this diagnosis?

   a.   92592 Hearing aid check; monaural
   b.   92596 Ear protector attenuation measurements
   c.   92609 Therapeutic services for the use of speech-generating device, including programming and modification
   d.   92610 Evaluation of oral and pharyngeal swallowing function

5.  The patient is experiencing jaundice.

   ICD-10-CM code: R17 Jaundice

   Which of the following CPT codes would be linked to this diagnosis?

   a.   82380 Carotene
   b.   82495 Chromium
   c.   80051 Electrolyte panel
   d.   80076 Hepatic function panel

6.  The patient is being evaluated for hypothyroidism.

   ICD-10-CM code: E03.9 Hypothyroidism

   Which of the following CPT codes would be linked to this diagnosis?

   a.   80061 Lipid panel
   b.   80438 Thyrotropin releasing hormone (TRH) stimulation panel; 1 hour
   c.   84443 Thyroid stimulating hormone (TSH)
   d.   84512 Troponin, qualitative

7.  Which of the following radiology CPT codes would be linked to a patient who has pneumonia? ICD-10-CM code: J18.9 Pneumonia

   a.   71020 Radiologic examination, chest, 2 views, frontal and lateral
   b.   71250 Computed tomography, thorax; without contrast material

   c.   75557 Cardiac magnetic resonance imaging for morphology and function; without contrast material

   d.   75741 Angiography, pulmonary, unilateral, selective, radiological supervision and interpretation

8.   Which of the following CPT codes would only be found on a male patient's claim form?

   a.   55040 Excision of hydrocele; unilateral

   b.   58300 Insertion of intrauterine device (IUD)

   c.   58760 Fimbrioplasty

   d.   59871 Removal of cerclage suture under anesthesia (other than local)

9.   Which of the following CPT codes would not pass the age edits for a 2-year-old child?

   a.   42820 Tonsillectomy and adenoidectomy; younger than age 12

   b.   43621 Gastrectomy; total; with Roux-en-Y reconstruction

   c.   49560 Repair initial incisional or ventral hernia; reducible

   d.   69436 Tympanostomy (requiring insertion of ventilating tube), general anesthesia

10.   Which of the following CPT codes would be linked to a patient who was being evaluated for stress incontinence?

   a.   51720 Bladder instillation of anticarcinogenic agent (including retention time)

   b.   51736 Simple uroflowmetry (UFR) (eg. stop-watch flow rate, mechanical uroflowmeter)

   c.   51880 Closure of cystostomy (separate procedure)

   d.   51980 Cutaneous vesicostomy

## Exercise 1.2: CPT Code Selection and Supportive Documentation

In the following exercise, review the assigned CPT code to determine if it is supported by the documentation. If the CPT code does not support the documentation, select a code that best represents the procedure/service.

1.   A surgeon performs a cystourethroscopy with dilation of a urethral stricture.
CPT Code: 52341

   **Answer:** _____

2.   The operative report states that the physician performed Strabismus surgery, requiring resection of the medial rectus muscle.
CPT Code: 67314

   **Answer:** _____

3.   The surgeon repairs a ruptured abdominal aortic aneurysm.
CPT Code 35092

   **Answer:** _____

4.   The surgeon performs a colonoscopy with removal of a polyp by hot biopsy forceps.
CPT Code: 45384

   **Answer:** _____

5.  A chiropractor documents that he performed osteopathic manipulation on the neck and back (lumbar/thoracic).
    CPT Code: 98925

    **Answer:** _____

6.  The Emergency Department physician extracted a piece of glass embedded in the muscle of the patient's foot.
    CPT Code: 28190

    **Answer:** _____

7.  A 45-year-old patient has a repair of an initial incarcerated inguinal hernia.
    CPT Code: 49521

    **Answer:** _____

8.  The physician performs a fine-needle aspiration biopsy of the testis with imaging guidance.
    CPT Code: 54500

    **Answer:** _____

9.  The surgeon performs an excision of a 1.5 cm deep intramuscular soft tissue tumor of the scalp.
    CPT Code 21011

    **Answer:** _____

10. The surgeon performs an ERCP with endoscopic retrograde removal of a stone from the biliary duct.
    CPT Code: 43275

    **Answer:** _____

## Exercise 1.3: Abstracting Documentation

An important part of the coding process is analyzing the documentation to support the appropriate coding selection. For the following exercises, read the operative report and underline the key documentation components that support the coding assignment. Assign a CPT code based on your documentation elements. Code the surgical CPT only.

**1.**

### Operative Report

PROCEDURE PERFORMED: Amniocentesis

REASON FOR PROCEDURE: The patient is a 30-year-old white female who is gravida 7, para 1, with intrauterine pregnancy at 36-4/7 weeks gestation. She was admitted in prodromal labor. She has gestational diabetes mellitus and an ultrasound suggesting fetal weight of greater than 10 pounds. The patient has been quite uncomfortable in recent weeks and is adamant about wanting to be delivered. In view of the gestational diabetes requiring insulin, I feel it important to document fetal lung maturity in a more or less elective delivery.

I discussed amniocentesis and the risks, benefits, and alternatives. After I answered her questions, she agreed to proceed with the procedure.

DESCRIPTION OF PROCEDURE: Under ultrasound guidance a 4 to 5 cm pocket of amniotic fluid was identified in the fundal left side. The abdomen was prepped and draped. Under ultrasound guidance a 22-gauge needle was inserted into this pocket and approximately 8 cc of fluid was obtained, which was lightly bloodstained. I attempted to aspirate more using a second syringe but was unable to get further fluid so the procedure was terminated.

ASSESSMENT AND PLAN: Postprocedure the fetal heart tracing was obtained and fetal heartbeat was in the 150s. Biophysical profile postprocedure was 10 out of 10. We will await the amniocentesis results, and if the l/s (lecithin/sphingomyelin) is mature, we will proceed with cesarean section.

**Abstract from Documentation:**

Refer to Amniocentesis in the Alphabetic Index. What documentation is needed to select the applicable code range? Underline the portion of the operative report that supports your answer.

CPT Code Assignment:

## 2.

### Operative Report

PREOPERATIVE DIAGNOSIS: Vastus medialis oblique tear, left knee

POSTOPERATIVE DIAGNOSIS: Traumatic bursal tear anterior left knee

OPERATIVE PROCEDURE: Inspection, evacuation of hematoma of bursal tissue, left knee

INDICATION: The patient is a 15-year-old male who injured his left knee while sliding into base during a baseball game. He developed immediate significant swelling and was unable to weight bear the first few days. I saw him and felt that he might have injured the vastus medialis muscle. An MRI scan of the knee was obtained which demonstrated what appeared to be torn tissue in that area. He has a palpable gap in the area. He has had otherwise good extensor function. We elected to proceed with surgical inspection of the area and repair of suspected muscle tear.

DESCRIPTION OF PROCEDURE: The patient received 1 g of Ancef. He was taken to the operating room and given a general anesthetic. I applied a tourniquet to the left thigh, and the left lower extremity was prepared with Betadine gel paint and draped out freely. The leg was exsanguinated with an elastic bandage.

I made a longitudinal incision beginning in the midportion of the patella and extending proximally 4 inches, and dissected down through fairly thick subcutaneous tissue directly into hematoma. This was evacuated. I then split swollen bursal tissue and determined that the underlying vastus medialis muscle and its quadriceps attachment was intact. Further exploration revealed intact capsular tissues and completely intact patellar tendon and quadriceps tendon structures. The bursal tissue was quite hemorrhagic and thickened. No other treatment was indicated.

The area was irrigated and I then closed the subcutaneous tissues with 2-0 Polysorb and the skin with staples. The incision was dressed with bacitracin ointment, 4x4 gauze, ABD pad, and an Ace wrap followed by a knee immobilizer.

The patient tolerated the procedure well. There were no complications. He was taken to recovery in good condition.

**Abstract from Documentation:**

Refer to Bursa, Knee in the Alphabetic Index. What are the choices?

Underline the supportive documentation.

CPT Code Assignment:

**3.**

### Operative Report

PREOPERATIVE DIAGNOSIS: Left upper lid laceration

POSTOPERATIVE DIAGNOSIS: Left upper lid laceration

PROCEDURE: Left upper lid laceration repair with exam under anesthesia

ANESTHESIA: General

COMPLICATIONS: There were no complications.

INDICATIONS: This 4-year-old child suffered a dog bite to his left upper lid that was unable to be repaired successfully in the emergency room. After obtaining informed consent, he was taken to the operating room.

DESCRIPTION OF PROCEDURE: The patient was prepped and draped in the usual sterile fashion. The wound margins were reapproximated using 6-0 absorbable suture and two lid margin sutures were placed using 6-0 silk. The injury was limited to the epidermis and part of the dermis. There was no structural damage to the blood vessels or deeper tissue layers. The lid was noted to be in good position, and then all skin lacerations were closed using a combination of 6-0 running and 6-0 interrupted nylon.

The patient then had his eye dilated, and exam under anesthesia was carried out using an indirect ophthalmoscope. There was no evidence of trauma to the globe or the posterior pole.

The patient was taken to the recovery room in good condition and will be sent home today to follow up in my office.

*Abstract from Documentation:*

Refer to Repair, Eyelid in the Alphabetic Index. What code range is applicable?

Underline the supportive documentation.

CPT Code Assignment:

**4.**

### Operative Report

PROCEDURE: Lumbar puncture

INDICATION: Paresthesias

DESCRIPTION OF PROCEDURE: Prior to the procedure, the relevant films were reviewed. Informed consent was obtained from the patient.

The patient was placed on the procedure table in prone position. The lower spine was examined with fluoroscopy. The area was then marked. The L3–L4 area was then prepped and draped in the usual fashion using chlorhexidine swab. Approximately 5 cc of 1 percent lidocaine was then used to anesthetize the area. A 20-gauge, 10 cm spinal needle was then advanced under direct fluoroscopic guidance into the thecal sac. The stylette was then removed, demonstrating adequate CSF backflow. Opening pressure was approximately 115 cm of water. Approximately 24 cc of fluid was removed without complication. Closing pressure was about 75 cm of water. Needle was then removed and bandage applied. 0.3 minutes of fluoroscopy time were utilized. The patient was instructed to lie in the horizontal position for at least 2 hours to decrease risk of spinal headache.

✎ *Abstract from Documentation:*

Refer to Puncture, Lumbar in the Alphabetic Index. What reference is provided in the index?

Follow the reference note. What is the difference between a diagnostic and therapeutic procedure?

What does the diagnosis paresthesias mean?

## 5.

### Operative Report

PROCEDURE: Upper endoscopy

INDICATION: The patient is a 45-year-old female who presents with 5 years of reflux symptoms. She has had some intermittent epigastric abdominal discomfort as well.

DESCRIPTION OF PROCEDURE: After obtaining informed consent and establishment of an intravenous line, the patient was positioned in the left lateral decubitus position. We used 10 mg of midazolam, 50 mcg of fentanyl, and supplemental oxygen at 2 liters per nasal cannula. She was monitored with pulse oximetry, continuous ECG tracing, and periodic blood pressure checks. A flexible video Olympus upper endoscope was passed through the oropharynx into the esophagus. The esophagus was unremarkable including the squamocolumnar junction at 36 cm from the incisors. Proximal gastric view including retroflexion showed minimal gastric valve laxity but was otherwise unremarkable. She had a series of three polyps in the general range of 5–7 mm in the mid gastric lumen, in line with the greater curvature of the stomach. One was more inflamed than the other two. All three were removed with standard snare polypectomy technique. The rest of the stomach was intact as was the pylorus, duodenal bulb, and second portion of the duodenum. All areas were resurveyed two additional times, and we simply identified no additional findings. She tolerated the procedure well and without apparent complication.

ASSESSMENT: Gastric polyps as mentioned above. Otherwise unremarkable upper endoscopy.

✎ *Abstract from Documentation:*

What is an upper endoscopy?

Did the physician visualize the structures or perform another procedure during the endoscopy?

Underline the supportive documentation.

CPT Code Assignment:

## 6.

### Operative Report

PREOPERATIVE DIAGNOSIS: Recurrent bladder tumor

POSTOPERATIVE DIAGNOSIS: Recurrent bladder tumor

PROCEDURE: Cystoscopy and transurethral resection of bladder tumor

ANESTHESIA: General

SUMMARY: Under satisfactory general anesthesia, the patient's genitalia were sterilely prepped and draped with the patient in lithotomy position.

A 24 French cystourethroscope was passed into the bladder under direct vision. The anterior urethra was normal. The prostatic urethra revealed slight encroachment of the lateral lobes of the prostate gland, but no severe obstruction, and the bladder neck was relatively open and pliable. The bladder was then carefully reviewed with four oblique and right-angle lenses. The only definite pathology noted was an area of mucosal hyperemia on the posterior bladder wall, at about its midpoint to the right of midline. This had a very slight papillary portion in its center. The whole area was no more than 2.5 cm in greatest diameter, and no other pathology was noted. The cystoscope was then removed, and sterile KY jelly was instilled into the urethra, which was then sounded through 30 French with van Buren sounds without difficulty.

A small continuous flow resectoscope was passed into the bladder, the obturator removed, and the working element with loop electrode fastened into position. A single pass of the resectoscope loop resected the entire abnormal mucosa described above, and this was irrigated from the bladder and submitted to pathology. The resection site and surrounding mucosa were then fulgurated with the loop electrode. The resectoscope was removed and replaced with a 20 French Foley catheter, which was left indwelling for 1 hour.

The patient tolerated the procedure well, blood loss was negligible, and he was sent to recovery in satisfactory and stable condition.

### Abstract from Documentation:

Refer to Bladder, Tumor in the Alphabetic Index. Based on the operative technique, what choice is applicable?

Underline the supportive documentation.

CPT Code Assignment:

## 7.

### Office Note

HISTORY: The patient complains of bilateral ear pain. She denies any decrease in hearing. She has marked cerumen impactions in both ear canals. It took extensive flushing before I was able to get out the wax on both sides. Both canals are now patent.

PHYSICAL EXAMINATION: Vital signs are stable and she is afebrile.

ASSESSMENT: Bilateral cerumen impactions

PLAN: I told her she should irrigate both ears once a week with peroxide and warm water.

### Abstract from Documentation:

What Alphabetic Index term can easily lead to the coding of this case?

Underline the supportive documentation.

CPT Code Assignment:

## 1.4: Crossword Puzzle

**Across**

2. Federal insurance for those over age 65

5. Modifier P4 found in this CPT section

8. CT scans found in this section of CPT

**Down**

1. Supports medical necessity

3. Agency administers Medicare

4. A new edition of CPT is published _____

6. Organization that publishes CPT

7. Number of digits in CPT code

# Chapter 2

# Application of the CPT System

## Exercise 2.1: Format and Organization of CPT

Match the correct definitions or descriptions.

1. _____ Complete list of modifiers          A. Appendix B

2. _____ Complete list of add-on codes       B. Category II code

3. _____ 0210T Speech audiometry             C. Appendix D
         threshold, automated

4. _____ Complete list of recent additions,  D. Appendix A
         deletions, and revisions

5. _____ 0503F Postpartum care visit         E. Category III code

## Exercise 2.2: Referencing *CPT Assistant*

Reference *CPT Assistant* to answer the following questions. Document the specific newsletter that addresses the question.

1. Refer to note below CPT code 29530. In the Professional Edition of CPT, what does the following note indicate?

   *CPT Assistant,* Feb 96:3, April 02:13, Jun 10:8, Aug 10:15

   **Answer:** _____

2. The surgeon removed three (3) stones from the ureter. Is it appropriate to report code 50945 (*Laparoscopy, surgical*; *ureterolithotomy*) for each stone removed from the ureter? (*CPT Assistant,* September 2006, pages 13–14)

   **Answer:** _____

3. The surgeon performed a nipple-sparing mastectomy. How is this reported to distinguish this procedure from a total mastectomy? (CPT Assistant, March 2015, page 5)

   **Answer:**_____

4. A physician performed an acoustic reflex test (code 92568) on only one ear. CPT guidelines state that all descriptors refer to testing both ears. What guidance does *CPT Assistant* provide from June 2004, page 10?

    **Answer:** _____

5. What is the correct code assignment for a bipolar radiofrequency hemorrhoidectomy? (*CPT Assistant*, April 2015, page 10)

    **Answer:** _____

6. What is the appropriate CPT code to report a band adjustment for a patient who previously had a lap band bariatric surgical procedure? (*CPT Assistant,* April 2006, page 19)

    **Answer:** _____

## Exercise 2.3: Application of CPT

Answer the following questions.

1. The physician performs a synovial biopsy of the metacarpophalangeal joint. Using the alphabetic index, what key word(s) lead you to the coding selection? What is the correct code?

    **Answer:** _____

2. The surgeon performed a radical resection of a 0.5 cm lesion of the back. The malignant neoplasm extended into the soft tissue. Refer to the term "Lesion" in the alphabetic index. What guidance does the alphabetic index provide? What is the correct code?

    **Answer:** _____

3. After an injection of Lidocaine, the surgeon performed a percutaneous tenotomy (Achilles tendon). Refer to 27605–27606. What is the correct code assignment?

    **Answer:** _____

4. Using cryosurgery, the surgeon removed four (4) dermatofibromas of the leg. Refer to CPT codes 17000–17250. What is the correct code assignment?

    **Answer:** _____

5. Refer to codes 57550–57556. The surgeon performed an excision of a cervical stump, vaginally, with repair of an enterocele. What is the correct code assignment?

    **Answer:** _____

Assign CPT codes for the following:

6. Insertion of a Foley catheter (temporary)

    **Answer:** _____

7. Percutaneous needle biopsy of the pancreas

    **Answer:** _____

8.  Aortic valve replacement utilizing a bovine prosthesis (performed with cardiopulmonary bypass)

    **Answer:** _____

9.  Laparoscopic Roux-en-Y gastric bypass procedure (150 cm)

    **Answer:** _____

10. Incision and drainage, hematoma, floor of the mouth, masticator space

    **Answer:** _____

## Exercise 2.4: Multiple Choice

1.  Reference CPT code section beginning with code 45330. What is the correct CPT code for removal of polyp using a snare?

    a.  45332
    b.  45333
    c.  45338
    d.  45346

2.  What documentation is necessary to code repair of an enterocele?

    a.  Under local or general anesthesia
    b.  Type of approach
    c.  Complicated or simple procedure
    d.  With or without exploration

3.  What documentation is necessary to code a thromboendarterectomy?

    a.  Name of artery
    b.  If a patch was used
    c.  Age of patient
    d.  Open or endoscopic procedure

4.  Reference CPT code section beginning with code 42820. What documentation is necessary to code a tonsillectomy procedure?

    a.  Size of tonsils
    b.  Surgical technique
    c.  Age of patient and if an adenoidectomy was also performed
    d.  Age of patient and type of approach

5.  Reference CPT code section beginning with code 21811. What documentation is necessary to code an open treatment of rib fractures?

    a.  Technique
    b.  Number of ribs
    c.  Severity of fracture
    d.  Type of repair

6.  The surgeon excised a benign tumor of the back, which extended into the subfascial layer. CPT code 21932 was assigned. What documentation is missing from this operative statement?

    a.  Morphology of the tumor
    b.  Exact location of the tumor
    c.  Surgical technique
    d.  Size of tumor

7.  The surgeon performed a repair of a left ruptured Achilles tendon. CPT code 27650 was assigned. What documentation is missing from this operative statement?

    a.  Primary or secondary repair and use of graft
    b.  Laterality
    c.  Simple or complicated
    d.  Partial or complete

8.  The physician excised a dermal cyst of the nose. What documentation is missing from this operative statement?

    a.  Primary or secondary procedure
    b.  Performed under local or general anesthesia
    c.  Depth of cyst
    d.  Biopsy performed during procedure

9.  Reference CPT codes 19081–19086 for breast biopsy. What documentation element(s) are needed for appropriate code assignment?

    a.  Size of lesion
    b.  Number of lesions and type of imaging
    c.  Size of lesions and type of imaging
    d.  Placement of localization device and type of imaging

10. Which code or code selection would be referenced for a male patient that is undergoing a breast reduction procedure?

    a.  19300
    b.  19301–19302
    c.  19303
    d.  19304

# Chapter 3

# Modifiers

## Exercise 3.1: Use of Modifiers

Match the modifier with the correct description.

1. _____ 3P     A. Physical status (anesthesia) modifier

2. _____ F4     B. HCPCS national modifier

3. _____ 73     C. Category II modifier

4. _____ P5     D. CPT modifier approved for hospital outpatient use only

5. _____ 53     E. CPT modifier *not* approved for hospital outpatient use

## Exercise 3.2: Select the Modifier Exercises

Read the following case scenarios, and indicate the appropriate modifier.

1. A 35-year-old patient seen in the physician's office for his yearly physical (CPT code 99395—*Preventive Medicine E/M)*. During the exam, the patient requests that the physician remove a mole on his shoulder. What CPT modifier would be appended to the 99395 to explain that the E/M service was unrelated to excision of the mole?

   **Answer:**_____

2. A patient is seen in a radiology clinic for an x-ray of the arm (73090). The films were sent to another radiologist (not affiliated with the clinic) to interpret and write the report. What HCPCS Level II modifier would be appended to the CPT code for the *services of the radiology clinic*?

   **Answer:**_____

3. A surgeon performed an esophageal dilation (43453) on a 4-week-old newborn that weighed 3.1 kg. What CPT modifier would be appended to the CPT code to describe this special circumstance?

   **Answer:**_____

4. A surgeon performed a tenolysis, extensor tendon of the right index finger (26445). What HCPCS Level II modifier should be appended to the CPT code?

    **Answer:**_____

5. An arthroscopic meniscectomy of the knee was planned for a patient. During the procedure, the scope was inserted, but the patient went into respiratory distress and the procedure was terminated. What CPT modifier would be appended to the CPT code (29880) for the *physician's services?*

    **Answer:**_____

### Exercise 3.3: Coding/Modifiers

Assign CPT codes with the appropriate modifier for the following.

### Case Study #1

A surgeon performed a carpal tunnel release (median nerve) on the left and right wrist.

    **Index:**_____

    **Code(s):** _____

### Case Study #2

A 45-year-old male was brought to the endoscopy suite for diagnostic EGD. Patient was prepped. After moving the patient to the procedure room, and prior to initiation of sedation, he develops significant hypotension, and the physician cancels the procedure. Code for *hospital services*.

    **Index:**_____

    **Code(s):** _____

### Case Study #3

The physician excised a chalazion of the left lower eyelid.

    **Index:** _____

    **Code(s):** _____

### Case Study #4

Patient presented for capsule endoscopy of the gastrointestinal tract. The ileum was not visualized.

    **Index:**_____

    **Code(s):** _____

### Case Study #5

A surgeon performed a tonsillectomy and adenoidectomy on a 25-year-old male. Four hours after leaving the surgery center, the patient presents to the clinic with a one-hour history of bleeding in the throat. The bleeding site was located; however, it was in a location that could not be treated outside the OR. The patient was taken back to the OR, by the same surgeon, for control of postoperative bleeding.

**Index:**_____

**Code(s):** _____

## Exercise 3.4: Multiple Choice Questions

1. Which of the following is recognized as a "physician only" modifier?

   a. 23
   b. 50
   c. 58
   d. 59

2. A surgeon performs a cholecystectomy on a morbidly obese female who has multiple adhesions. Documentation supports that the surgeon spent over two hours performing lysis of adhesions before the cholecystectomy could be performed. Which of the following modifiers would be applicable for the surgeon to communicate this circumstance?

   a. 22
   b. 26
   c. 51
   d. 59

3. The patient had a 2.2 cm malignant lesion excised from the neck (CPT code 11623) and another from the scalp (2.5 cm) during the same operative episode (CPT code 11623). Which modifier would be appended to this code to explain reporting it twice?

   a. 22
   b. 27
   c. 76
   d. 77

4. The physician removes part of the patient's right big toenail (CPT code 11750). Which modifier should be appended to this code?

   a. TA
   b. RT
   c. T5
   d. 76

5. A surgeon asks a colleague to assist him in a complicated surgical procedure because his resident is not available. Which modifier is appropriate for this circumstance?

   a. 22
   b. 26
   c. 54
   d. 82

6. A surgeon performed a laparoscopic gastric lap band procedure (CPT code 43770). Another physician performed the postoperative management for this patient. What

modifier would be appended to the code for the physician following the patient postoperatively?

a. 24
b. 54
c. 55
d. 57

7. Which of the following demonstrates inappropriate use of a modifier?

a. 69210-50 Ear wax removal, both ears
b. 40843-50 Vestibuloplasty, posterior, bilateral
c. 27465-LT Osteoplasty, shortening of femur, left
d. 66700-LT Ciliary body destruction using diathermy, left eye

8. The hospital technician performs a simple cystometrogram (CPT code 51725). A physician not employed by the hospital reads the results and dictates the final report. Which modifier is appropriate for the physician?

a. 25
b. 26
c. 59
d. TC

9. Patient has a transurethral resection of the prostate (TURP) and is discharged home with no complaints. Two days later, the patient returns to the surgeon's office complaining of abdominal pain. The diagnostic studies reveal a kidney stone. Which of the following modifiers appropriately describes this office visit during the global period?

a. 24
b. 25
c. 55
d. 78

10. A patient had a mastectomy several weeks ago due to cancer. She is now readmitted for a scheduled insertion of breast implants (CPT code 19342). Which modifier is appropriate for this case?

a. 26
b. 32
c. 54
d. 58

# Chapter 4

# Surgery: Part I

Answers to the exercises in this section will not apply modifier 51 (multiple procedures) or sequencing for claims submission. The focus of these exercises is to practice accurate assignment of CPT codes without regard to payer guidelines. The answers will include use of lateral modifiers (such as RT and FA) and Modifier 50 for bilateral. For the purposes of instruction, this book uses a dash to separate each five-character CPT code from its two-character modifier. However, dashes are not used in actual code assignments and reimbursement claims.

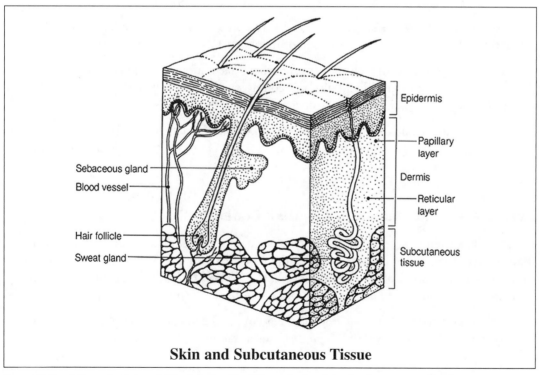

**Skin and Subcutaneous Tissue**

Source: National Cancer Institute. n.d. VisualsOnline. Don Bliss, artist. http://visualsonline.cancer.gov/details .cfm?imageid=4362.

# Integumentary System Exercises

### Exercise 4.1: Medical Terminology Review

Match the medical terms with the definitions.

1. ____ biopsy
2. ____ basal cell carcinoma
3. ____ cryosurgery
4. ____ debridement
5. ____ lipoma

A. freeze tissue
B. removal of damaged tissue from wound
C. removal of a piece of tissue for examination
D. malignant neoplasm
E. benign neoplasm

### Exercise 4.2: Clinical Concepts

Fill in the blanks for the following scenarios. Choose from one of the answers provided in parentheses.

1. The 3.0 cm lipoma extended into the tendon of the shoulder. The code for this procedure would be selected from the _____ chapter (integumentary or musculoskeletal).

2. The physician uses a laser to remove a lesion of the back. For coding purposes, this would be classified as _____ (excision or destruction).

3. The surgeon removes a 2.0 cm basal cell carcinoma of the neck. The lesion would be defined as _____ (benign or malignant).

4. The physician sutured a 3 cm × 2 cm superficial laceration of the knee. The wound required removal of gravel and dirt. For coding purposes, this would be classified as _____ (simple or intermediate repair).

5. The skin graft required harvesting healthy skin from the patient's right thigh to cover the defect of the arm. This type of graft is called _____ (autograft, allograft, or xenograft).

### Exercise 4.3: Integumentary System Coding Drill

For all coding exercises, review the documentation and underline key term(s). Identify the terms used to look up the code selection in the Alphabetic Index. Assign CPT codes to the following cases. If applicable, append CPT/HCPCS Level II modifiers. In some cases, the student will be prompted to answer questions about the case study.

1. A surgeon reports that the patient has a 2.5-cm basal cell carcinoma of the chin. The excision required removal of 0.5 cm margins around the lesion.

   **Index:**_____

   **Code(s):**_____

2. Operative Note: After local anesthesia was administered, the site was cleansed and an incision was made in the center of the sebaceous cyst. The cyst was drained and irrigated with a sterile solution. Diagnosis: sebaceous cyst of back.

   **Index:**_____

   **Code(s):**_____

3. A patient is seen in the Emergency Department after an accident. A 4.0-cm deep wound of the upper arm (located in area of non-muscle fascia) required a layered closure, and a 1.0 cm superficial laceration of the left cheek was repaired.

   **Index:**_____

   **Code(s):**_____

4. Patient has a diagnosis of a decubitus ulcer of the leg. The surgeon debrided the necrotic tissue that extended down to and included part of the muscle.

   **Index:**_____

   **Code(s):**_____

5. Operative Procedure: Shaving of a 0.75-cm pyogenic granuloma of the neck.

   **Index:**_____

   **Code(s):**_____

6. With the use of a YAG laser, the surgeon removed a 2.0-cm giant congenital melanocytic nevus of the leg. Pathology confirmed that the lesion was premalignant.

   **Index:**_____

   **Code(s):**_____

7. Operative Note: Patient seeking treatment for a cyst of right breast. A 21-gauge needle was inserted into the cyst. The white, cystic fluid was aspirated and the needle withdrawn. Pressure was applied to the wound and the site covered with a bandage.

   **Index:**_____

   **Code(s):**_____

8. The surgeon fulgurates a 0.5-cm superficial basal cell carcinoma of the back.

   **Index:**_____

   **Code(s):**_____

9. A physician performs a simple avulsion of the nail plate, second and third digits of the right foot.

   **Index:**_____

   **Code(s):**_____

10. With the use of electrocauterization, the physician removed 18 skin tags from the patient's neck and shoulders.

    **Index:**_____

    **Code(s):**_____

## Exercise 4.4: Case Studies—Integumentary System Operative and Emergency Department Reports

**1.**

### Dermatology Office Note

The patient was seen in the office for an annual skin exam. He has been treated for actinic keratosis in the past. The examination revealed three actinic keratosis of the forehead. The lesions were treated with liquid nitrogen. The patient was given wound care instructions.

*Abstract from Documentation:*

What type of lesion was removed?

How was it removed?

What other documentation is needed to support the code assignment?

*Time to Code:*

**Index:**_____

**Coding Assignment:**_____

**2.**

### Operative Note

This 59-year-old male developed a sebaceous cyst on his right upper back. After ensuring a comfortable position, the skin surrounding the cyst was infiltrated with 0.5 percent Xylocaine with epinephrine to achieve local anesthesia. An elliptical incision surrounding the cyst was made; total excised diameter of 5.0 cm. The cyst wall was dissected free from the surrounding tissues. Hemostasis was obtained and the wound was copiously irrigated. The wound was closed with 3-0 Vicryl, figure-of-eight stitches.

*Abstract from Documentation:*

What type of lesion was removed?

How was it removed?

What is the excised diameter of the lesion?

Did the physician close the wound routinely or was there a layered closure?

*Time to Code:*

**Index:**_____

**Coding Assignment:**_____

**3.**

## Operative Report

PREOPERATIVE DIAGNOSIS: 1.5 cm malignant melanoma, right heel

POSTOPERATIVE DIAGNOSIS: Same

OPERATION: Wide local excision with split thickness skin graft from the left thigh

ANESTHESIA: Spinal

INDICATIONS: This 72-year-old patient has a 1.5-cm malignant lesion of the left heel. He has agreed to a wide local excision.

PROCEDURE: The patient was taken to the operating room, prepped and draped in the usual sterile fashion. A 1/20 of an inch thick split-thickness skin graft (7 cm × 7 cm) was harvested from the left thigh and preserved. Next, the lesion, which was on the medial aspect of the right heel, was excised with 2.5 cm margins down to and including some of the plantar fascia. Total excised diameter was 6.5 cm. Hemostasis was achieved with 2-0 Tycron sutures and the cautery. After suitable hemostasis was obtained, the wound margins were advanced with interrupted sutures of 2-0 chromic and then the skin graft was placed.

The skin graft was approximated to the skin using interrupted running sutures of 4-0 chromic, and then holes were punched in the skin graft to permit egress of serous fluid. Then, a bolster dressing of cotton batting wrapped in Owen's gauze was placed over the skin graft site and secured to the skin with multiple sutures tied over it to 2-0 Tycron. The skin graft donor site was wrapped with Owen's gauze and two moistened ABD pads and wrapped with a Kerlix and an Ace wrap. The patient tolerated the procedure well and was transported awake and alert to the recovery room in excellent condition.

*Abstract from Documentation:*

What procedure was performed?

What are the excised diameter, location, and type (malignant/benign) of lesion?

What is the coding guideline for excision of lesion with subsequent skin replacement surgery? Do you code both or just the skin graft?

What type of skin graft was performed? Adjacent? Skin replacement? Autograft? Cultured tissue?

Was the skin graft full thickness or split thickness?

For coding purposes, identify site of defect, size, and type of graft.

*Time to Code:*

**Index for Excision of Lesion:**_____

**Index for Skin Graft:**_____

**Code(s):**_____

**4.**

## Emergency Department Record

CHIEF COMPLAINT: Scalp laceration

HISTORY OF PRESENT ILLNESS: Patient is an 88-year-old white female who lost her balance and fell in her room today, hitting her head and sustaining a laceration of her right scalp. No loss of consciousness. No syncope. No neck pain. No vomiting. She has been acting normally since the injury, according to her daughter.

PAST MEDICAL HISTORY: Hypertension, dementia

MEDICATIONS: Colace, iron, hydrochlorothiazide, Paxil

ALLERGIES: None

IMMUNIZATIONS: Not up to date

PHYSICAL EXAMINATION:

GENERAL: Alert female in no acute distress

HEAD, EARS, EYES, NOSE, AND THROAT: There is a 3.5 cm full skin thickness scalp laceration. Minimal swelling. No deformity. Pupils are equal and reactive to light. Extraocular muscles intact. Tympanic membranes normal. Oropharynx negative.

NECK: Supple. Nontender.

HEART: Regular. No murmurs or gallops noted.

LUNGS: Breath sounds equal bilaterally and clear.

EXTREMITIES: Atraumatic. Full range of motion.

NEUROLOGICAL: Awake, alert, and oriented to person. Not to place or time. No focal motor. Moves all extremities symmetrically. Deep tendon reflexes 1+.

PROCEDURE: Anesthesia local injection 3 cc lidocaine with epinephrine. Prepped. Explored. No foreign body noted. Closed in a single layer with interrupted staples. Polysporin ointment was placed.

DIAGNOSIS: 3.5 cm simple scalp laceration.

DISPOSITION AND PLAN: Wound care instructions; head injury instructions; staples out in 10–12 days.

*Abstract from Documentation:*

What was the treatment for the laceration?

What key pieces of documentation are needed to code this case?

*Time to Code:*

**Index:**_____

**Code(s):**_____

**5.**

## Operative Report

PREOPERATIVE DIAGNOSIS: Epidermoidal nevus of scalp

POSTOPERATIVE DIAGNOSIS: Epidermoidal nevus of scalp

The patient was brought to the operating room suite and made comfortable in a supine position on the table. The area was infiltrated with 1 percent lidocaine with 1:100,000 parts epinephrine. The area was then prepped and draped in the usual sterile fashion. A #15 blade was used to remove a small portion of the 2.0 cm lesion, which was carefully labeled and sent to Pathology for exam. The rest of the nevus was shaved off at the level of the dermis. Hemostasis was achieved with cautery. A dressing of Gelfoam soaked in thrombin was placed over this, and the patient allowed to return to the Recovery Room with stable vital signs. The estimated blood loss was less than 15 cc, and it was replaced with crystalloid solution only. Sponge, needle, and instrument counts were reported as correct.

*Abstract from Documentation:*

How was the lesion removed?

Was the lesion benign or malignant?

What key pieces of documentation are needed for this type of treatment?

*Time to Code:*

**Index:**_____

**Code(s):**_____

# Musculoskeletal System Exercises

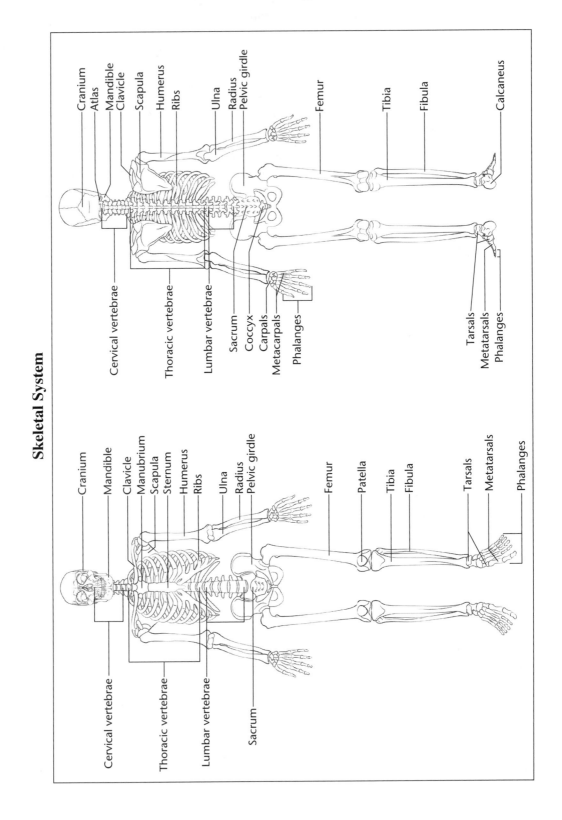

## Exercise 4.5: Crossword Puzzle

**Across**

3. Bones of hand

5. Near center of body

6. Cartilage in knee joint

7. Knee bone

**Down**

1. Away from center of body

2. Bone of upper arm

4. Bones of fingers or toes

## Exercise 4.6: Clinical Concepts

Fill in the blanks to the following scenarios. Choose from one of the two answers provided in parentheses.

1. The Radiology Report revealed that the displaced fracture did not heal. This fracture would be referred to as _____ (nonunion, malunion).

2. At bedside, the Emergency Department physician realigned the fracture. The manipulation is known as _____ (closed, open).

3. The patient has advanced arthritis of the elbow joint. The physician performs a fusion of the joint to provide stability. This procedure is referred to as _____ (arthrodesis, tenolysis).

4. During the procedure, the surgeon encountered numerous restrictive bands of scar tissue. For this condition, you would expect to see _____ documented in the health record (lysis of adhesions, synovectomy).

5. The talus bone is located in the _____ (knee, ankle).

## Exercise 4.7: Musculoskeletal System Coding Drill

Review the documentation and underline key term(s). Identify the terms used to look up the code selection in the Alphabetic Index. Assign CPT codes to the following cases. If applicable, append CPT modifiers.

1. A patient is diagnosed with osteochondroma of the right clavicle. The surgeon excises the tumor.

    **Index:**_____

    **Code(s):**_____

2. The patient is seen in the outpatient surgery department for a comminuted right supracondylar femoral fracture. An open reduction and internal fixation of the right supracondylar femur fracture was performed.

    **Index:**_____

    **Code(s):**_____

3. The surgeon performed a percutaneous tenotomy of the left hand, second digit and third digit.

    **Index:**_____

    **Code(s):**_____

4. The surgeon performed an arthroscopy of the right knee with medial meniscectomy.

    **Index:**_____

    **Code(s):**_____

5. The patient had been diagnosed with an infected abscess extending below the fascia of the knee. The surgeon performed an incision and drainage of the abscess.

   **Index:**_____

   **Code(s):**_____

6. Surgeon performed an arthroscopy of the right knee, with limited synovectomy and shaving of articular cartilage.

   **Index:**_____

   **Code(s):**_____

7. The surgeon performed a closed reduction of a scaphoid fracture.

   **Index:**_____

   **Code(s):**_____

8. The surgeon performs an open reduction with insertion of intramedullary rod of the right tibial shaft.

   **Index:**_____

   **Code(s):**_____

9. Patient treated for posttraumatic osteoarthritis of right knee. The surgeon performed a total knee arthroplasty. All components were removed, and surfaces were irrigated. The components were cemented into place, beginning with a femora component and followed by the tibial component and then the patellar component.

   **Index:**_____

   **Code(s):**_____

10. Patient has the diagnosis of wet gangrene of the right great toe. The physician performs an amputation of the metatarsophalangeal joint with removal of the right great toe.

    **Index:**_____

    **Code(s):**_____

## Exercise 4.8: Case Studies—Musculoskeletal System Operative and Emergency Department Reports

**1.**

### Emergency Department Record

The patient is a 67-year-old female who presents here after a fall from the stairs. She complains of pain in her right ankle. Examination reveals a noted open fracture with distal fibular fracture, displaced and exposed approximately 10 cm of the bone.

EMERGENCY DEPARTMENT COURSE: The patient was given IV fluids, morphine for pain, and Phenergan. The patient was given conscious sedation for placing the bone back within the ankle to prevent desiccation.

I contacted Dr. K. Lee, orthopedic services at Memorial, who was going to admit the patient for further treatment.

PROCEDURE NOTE: The patient was given Versed and morphine conscious sedation. The ankle was reduced, wet dressings applied, and a splint placed until further reduction can be performed.

✎ *Abstract from Documentation:*

What is the location of the fracture?

What services did the emergency department physician perform?

🕐 *Time to Code:*

**Index:**_____

**Code(s):**_____

## 2.

### Operative Report

PREOPERATIVE DIAGNOSIS: Right arm mass

POSTOPERATIVE DIAGNOSIS: Right arm mass

PROCEDURE: Excision, right arm mass

INDICATIONS: This is a 42-year-old woman who presents with palpable enlarging uncomfortable 5.0 cm mass in the right upper arm. After discussion, she agreed with excision of the area.

ANESTHESIA: Local with 1 percent plain Lidocaine and sedation

BLOOD LOSS: Minimal

DETAILS OF PROCEDURE: After informed consent was obtained, the patient was taken to the operating room and placed on the table in supine position. Sedation was administered and the right arm was prepped with Betadine solution and draped sterilely. The palpable mass was identified, and an elliptical skin incision was created over the mass along its axis, and the underlying mass was excised in its entirety to the level of muscle fascia. It appeared to be most consistent with being multilobulated lipoma. It was forwarded to Pathology. The wound was inspected for hemostasis, which was excellent. The deep tissues were approximated with interrupted 3-0 Vicryl, and running 4-0 Monocryl subcuticular stitch was used to approximate the skin edges. Benzoin, Steri-Strips, and sterile dressing were applied. She was awakened from sedation and returned to the recovery room in stable condition, having tolerated the procedure well.

### Pathology Report

FINAL DIAGNOSIS: Soft tissue mass of right upper arm. Lipoma

✎ *Abstract from Documentation:*

What was the final diagnosis from the pathologist?

How deep did the mass extend?

What was the treatment for the mass?

Is this a removal of a skin tumor or did it extend into the musculoskeletal area?

🕐 *Time to Code:*

**Index:**_____

**Code(s):**_____

---

## 3.

### Operative Report

PREOPERATIVE DIAGNOSIS: Mechanical complication from internal 0.062 K-wire, first metatarsal, right foot

POSTOPERATIVE DIAGNOSIS: Same

PROCEDURE: Removal of K-wire, right foot

The patient was brought to the operating room and placed on the table in supine position under the influence of IV sedation. Local anesthesia was administered. The right foot was prepped and draped in the usual sterile fashion. The right foot was exsanguinated with an Esmarch bandage, and his ankle tourniquet was inflated. A 1-cm dorsal medial skin incision was made directly over the palpable head of the pin. The incision was deepened bluntly, taking care to preserve and retract neurovascular structures. The periosteum was sharply incised from the underlying pin, and the pin was removed with a large straight hemostat. The wound was flushed with copious amounts of sterile normal saline. The skin was reapproximated with a 5-0 Vicryl in a subcuticular fashion. The site was dressed with Xeroform gauze and a dry sterile compression dressing. 4 cc of 0.5 percent Marcaine was injected for postoperative anesthesia.

✎ *Abstract from Documentation:*

What is a K-wire?

What procedure was performed for this patient?

🕐 *Time to Code:*

**Index:**_____

**Code(s):**_____

---

## 4.

### Emergency Department Report

CHIEF COMPLAINT: Left wrist injury

HISTORY OF PRESENT ILLNESS: The patient is a 5-year-old female that presents in the ED after accidentally falling off her bicycle. She tried to brace her fall with her left wrist and now says there is pain that increases with movement. She had no other injuries. There were no head injuries.

VITAL SIGNS: Blood pressure 117/72, temperature 97.8, pulse 106, respirations 20.

GENERAL: The patient is alert, oriented × 3. In no acute distress seated in the hospital bed.

EXTREMITIES: Physical exam of the left upper extremity reveals no deformity. To palpation, the patient has tenderness of the distal radius and ulna. No tenderness to palpation of the hand. Range of motion is limited in the wrist but intact in the hand and elbow with no tenderness in the elbow.

EMERGENCY DEPARTMENT COURSE: X-ray of the left wrist revealed a Buckle fracture of the distal radius and ulna. Volar splint and sling were applied. The patient was discharged to follow-up with the Orthopedic Group.

ASSESSMENT: Buckle fracture left distal radius and ulna

PLAN: Ice and elevate, return if worse, follow-up with orthopedics in 2–3 days, Tylenol with codeine elixir p.r.n. for pain was prescribed.

### ✐ Abstract from Documentation:

What was the treatment for the fracture?

### ⏱ Time to Code:

**Index:**_____

**Code(s):**_____

---

## 5.

### Operative Report

PREOPERATIVE DIAGNOSIS: Left middle trigger finger

POSTOPERATIVE DIAGNOSIS: Left middle trigger finger

PROCEDURE: Tenolysis

Under satisfactory IV block anesthesia, the patient was prepped and draped in the usual fashion. A transverse incision was made parallel to the distal palmar crease overlying the middle finger, and the wound was then deepened by sharp dissection and blunt dissection, being very careful to preserve all blood vessels intact and not to disturb the neurovascular bundle. The flexor tendon sheath was identified and divided longitudinally for a distance of approximately 1/5 cm. There was no bow stringing of the flexor tendon following this, and there was good gliding motion of the flexor tendon passively without any obstruction. The patient then had closure of the subcutaneous tissue with one interrupted 4-0 plain catgut suture, and the skin was closed with three interrupted 4-0 nylon vertical mattress sutures. Betadine ointment and dry sterile dressing were applied. Bulky hand dressing was applied. The patient, having tolerated the procedure well, had the tourniquet released without any untoward effects and was returned to the ambulatory unit in satisfactory condition.

### ✐ Abstract from Documentation:

What is a trigger finger?

What was performed to correct the condition?

### ⏱ Time to Code:

**Index:**_____

**Code(s):**_____

## 6.

### Operative Report

PREOPERATIVE DIAGNOSIS: Torn left Achilles tendon

POSTOPERATIVE DIAGNOSIS: Torn left Achilles tendon

OPERATION PERFORMED: Open repair of torn left Achilles tendon

INDICATIONS: This 22-year-old male was playing tennis when he suffered a complete rupture of the left Achilles tendon.

DETAILS OF PROCEDURE: The patient was given 2 grams of Ancef IV piggyback prior to coming to the operative suite. After induction of general anesthesia, the patient was placed in prone position. The entire left lower extremity was prepped and draped in the sterile fashion.

A posteromedial and longitudinal incision was made along the medial edge of the Achilles tendon measuring about 3 inches. Dissection continued down to reveal a complete rupture of the Achilles tendon. A four-core repair of running interlocking type Kessler suture was performed with #2 FiberWire. Excellent repair was achieved.

The wound was closed in layers and dressings were placed with Xeroform 4 × 4s. The patient was sent to recovery in stable condition.

*Abstract from Documentation:*

Where is the Achilles tendon located?

What was performed to correct the condition?

*Time to Code:*

**Index:**_____

**Code(s):**_____

# Respiratory System Exercises

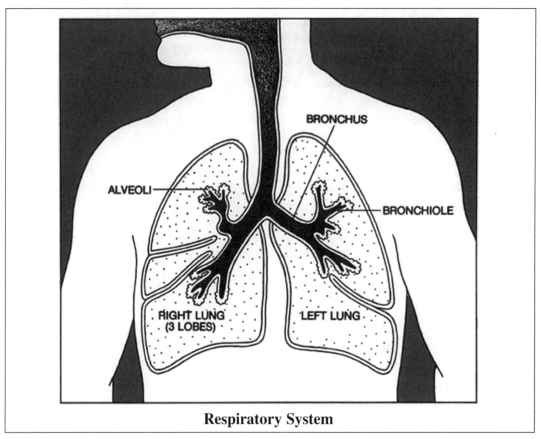

**Respiratory System**

Source: National Cancer Institute. n.d. VisualsOnline. Unknown photographer/artist. http://visualsonline.cancer.gov/details.cfm?imageid=1775.

### Exercise 4.9: Medical Terminology Review

Match the following terms with the correct definition.

1. ____ larynx          A. major air passages of lungs

2. ____ esophagus       B. connects mouth to esophagus

3. ____ bronchus        C. structure leads from throat to stomach

4. ____ pharynx         D. a bone in the nose

5. ____ ethmoid         E. voice box

## Exercise 4.10: Clinical Concepts

Fill in the blanks to the following scenarios. Choose from one of the two answers provided in parentheses.

1. A patient is suspected of a lesion on the vocal cord. The physician would most likely perform a _____ for further diagnosis and/or treatment (laryngoscopy, bronchoscopy).

2. The patient is experiencing sinus blockages in the area between the eye sockets. These sinuses are called _____ (frontal, ethmoid).

3. The patient has pleural fluid that must be removed. The physician would most likely perform a _____ to remove the fluid (pneumocentesis, pneumonectomy).

4. A piece of candy is lodged in the back of the patient's throat. The physician would make the diagnosis of foreign body in the _____ (pharynx, trachea).

5. A patient is seen in the Emergency Department for epistaxis and the physician performs cautery. The purpose of this procedure is to _____ (remove the nasal blockage, control nasal hemorrhage).

## Exercise 4.11: Respiratory System Coding Drill

Review the documentation and underline key term(s). Identify the terms used to look up the code selection in the Alphabetic Index. Assign CPT codes to the following cases. If applicable, assign CPT/HCPCS Level II modifiers.

1. Surgeon performs an endoscopic anterior ethmoidectomy.

   **Index:**_____

   **Code(s):**_____

2. Physician removes an indwelling tunneled pleural catheter with cuff.

   **Index:**_____

   **Code(s):**_____

3. A patient is seen in the Emergency Department for epistaxis. Physician performs an anterior packing of left nasal passage.

   **Index:**_____

   **Code(s):**_____

4. A physician performs a bilateral nasal endoscopy with polypectomy

   **Index:**_____

   **Code(s):**_____

5. A patient is seen with difficulty breathing due to deviated nasal septum. The surgeon performs a submucous resection of the septum.

   **Index:**_____

   **Code(s):**_____

6. The surgeon performs a thoracentesis by placing a needle under fluoroscopic guidance through the chest wall into the pleural space to withdraw fluid, which will be sent to the lab for analysis.

   **Index:**_____

   **Code(s):**_____

7. A patient was diagnosed with squamous cell carcinoma of the larynx. The surgeon performed a supraglottic laryngectomy with radical neck dissection to remove the metastasis to the lymph nodes.

   **Index:**_____

   **Code(s):**_____

8. The surgeon performed a thoracoscopy for a wedge resection of the lung.

   **Index:**_____

   **Code(s):**_____

9. With the use of an operating microscope, the surgeon performs a direct laryngoscopy for removal of a piece of a toothpick.

   **Index:**_____

   **Code(s):**_____

10. Bronchoscopy with multiple transbronchial lung biopsies taken of the right upper lobe.

   **Index:**_____

   **Code(s):**_____

## Exercise 4.12: Case Studies—Respiratory System Operative Reports

**1.**

### Operative Report

PREOPERATIVE DIAGNOSIS: Persistent upper lobe infiltrate

POSTOPERATIVE DIAGNOSIS: Persistent upper lobe infiltrate

PROCEDURE: Bronchoscopy

The patient was brought to the endoscopy suite and anesthesia was administered. After the patient was placed in supine position, the fiberoptic bronchoscope was passed through the left nostril without difficulty. The upper airway, vocal cords, and upper trachea were unremarkable. Examination of the left bronchial tree demonstrated no abnormalities. The right upper lobe also appeared normal. The mucosa surrounding the right upper lobe appeared normal. The rest of the right bronchial tree was unremarkable. Next, we obtained brush specimens from the right upper lobe to send to cytology. We obtained bronchial washings from the right upper lobe as well and sent it to cytology. The patient tolerated the procedure well.

*Abstract from Documentation:*

What type of endoscopy was performed?

What was performed during the endoscopic procedure?

*Time to Code:*

**Index:**_____

**Code(s):**_____

## 2.

### Operative Report

PREOPERATIVE DIAGNOSIS: Abnormal chest x-ray and CT scan revealed possible malignant neoplasm of the right upper lobe. Patient is a heavy smoker.

POSTOPERATIVE DIAGNOSIS: Squamous cell carcinoma, upper right lobe

PROCEDURE: Flexible Bronchoscopy

PROCEDURE: The patient was prepped, draped, and after adequate anesthesia, the scope was inserted through the right nares. The scope was advanced further. The vocal cords were normal. Carina was normal. The right main bronchus up into the upper middle and lower lobe bronchi were visualized. The right upper lobe showed an obstructive lesion. Other segments of the middle and lower lobe bronchi were normal. Biopsies and brushings were taken from the right upper lobe bronchus. The patient tolerated the procedure well.

*Abstract from Documentation:*

What procedures were performed during the endoscopic procedure?

*Time to Code:*

**Index:**_____

**Code(s):**_____

## 3.

### Operative Report

PREOPERATIVE DIAGNOSIS: Bilateral true vocal cord lesions

POSTOPERATIVE DIAGNOSIS: Bilateral true vocal cord intracordal cyst

OPERATION: Microlaryngoscopy and biopsy

INDICATIONS: This is a 58-year-old man with a history of tobacco use who has had a hoarse voice for the past couple of years. The patient also has an alcohol history. Considering his risk factors and hoarseness, the patient agreed to undergo the surgical procedure to not only better define the lesion but also the nature of the lesion by getting biopsies for pathology.

OPERATIVE FINDINGS: Bilateral intracordal mucoid cysts without any evidence of ulcerations or other mass lesions of the vocal cords.

DETAILS OF PROCEDURE: Patient was brought to the operating room and laid supine on the operating table. After adequate anesthesia, a dedo laryngoscope was used to survey the supraglottic area. Once other abnormalities were ruled out, attention was then directed to the true vocal cords. The patient was then suspended using the dedo laryngoscope, and the operating microscope was then brought into the field. Under binocular microscopy, the nature of the lesions was better assessed. It appeared that the vocal cords themselves were smooth and very soft to palpation. A Boucher retractor was then used to grasp the right true vocal cord, and a sickle knife was then used to make an incision laterally. Left-going scissors were then used to create a submucosal flap. The mucoid mass was then extruded and grasped with the nontraumatic graspers, and the scissors were then used to dissect the full extent of the mass. The suction was then used to verify the operative site on the right true vocal cord, and once adequate resection was achieved, the mucosal flap was then placed back onto normal position. Attention was then given toward the left intracordal cyst, which was not as prominent as the right. Again using left nontraumatic graspers, the left true vocal cord was grasped and medialized with enough tension so that the sickle knife could be used to make an incision laterally. A submucosal flap was then developed using the suction tip, and the mucosal cyst was then identified and carefully excised from the tissues of the true vocal cord, careful not to violate the ligaments or get into the vocals muscle. At this point, once adequate excision was obtained, the mucosal flap was then replaced. At this time, Afrin-soaked pledgets were then used to create adequate hemostasis. The Afrin-soaked pledgets were then removed at the conclusion of the operation. The operating microscope was then taken out of the field. The patient was then taken out of suspension and his care handed over to the anesthesiologist.

✎ *Abstract from Documentation:*

What type of endoscopy was performed?

What was performed during the endoscopic procedure?

🕐 *Time to Code:*

**Index:**_____

**Code(s):**_____

**4.**

## Operative Report

PREOPERATIVE DIAGNOSIS: Chronic laryngitis with polypoid disease

POSTOPERATIVE DIAGNOSIS: Same

PROCEDURE: Direct laryngoscopy and removal of polyps from both cords

PROCEDURE DETAIL: After adequate premedication, the patient was taken to the operating room and placed in supine position. The Jako laryngoscope was inserted. There were noted to be large polyps on both vocal cords, essentially obstructing the glottic airway. The polyps were excised from the left cord first. They were removed up to the anterior third, but the anterior tip was not removed on the left side. The polyps were removed from the right cord up to the anterior commissure. There was minimal bleeding noted. The patient was extubated and sent to recovery in good condition.

✎ *Abstract from Documentation:*

What type of endoscopy was performed?

What procedure was performed during the endoscopy?

🕐 *Time to Code:*

**Index:**_____

**Code(s):**_____

## 5.

### Operative Report

PREOPERATIVE DIAGNOSIS: Recurrent right malignant pleural effusion

POSTOPERATIVE DIAGNOSIS: Recurrent right malignant pleural effusion

PROCEDURE PERFORMED: Right thoracoscopic pleurodesis

FINDINGS: The patient had approximately 2 L of straw-colored pleural fluid.

DESCRIPTION OF PROCEDURE: The patient was taken to the operating room, placed in the supine position, and was administered a general endotracheal anesthesia through a double-lumen endotracheal tube. The patient was then placed in the left lateral decubitus position with the right side up. The patient's skin was prepped, and she was draped in the usual sterile fashion. An incision was made in the midclavicular line, and the chest was entered. Finger probe was swept in the pleural cavity, and there were no lung adhesions. The patient had approximately 2 L of straw-colored fluid evacuated. A trocar was then placed into the chest cavity, and a 30-degree laparoscope was inserted. There was no lung injury noted.

The patient had two additional 15 mm ports placed in a triangulating fashion. These were placed under visualization of the thoracoscope. A Bovie scratch pad was then used to mechanically pleurodesis the parietal pleura. The patient had what appeared to be adequate abrasions to most of the surfaces of the thoracic cavity. The lung was inspected; again, no injuries were identified. A 36 French chest tube was then placed into the apex through the inferior and medial most trocar site. The thoracic fascia was then reapproximated in 0-Polysorb interrupted fashion. The skin was closed with staples. The chest tube was secured with a 0-Polysorb suture. The chest tube was secured to a pleurovac. The patient's wounds were infiltrated with 0.5 percent Marcaine with epinephrine with a total of 10 mL being injected. The patient tolerated the procedure well. She was transported to the recovery room in satisfactory condition.

✏ *Abstract from Documentation:*

What is Pleurodesis?

🕐 *Time to Code:*

**Index:**_____

**Code(s):**_____

# Cardiovascular System Exercises

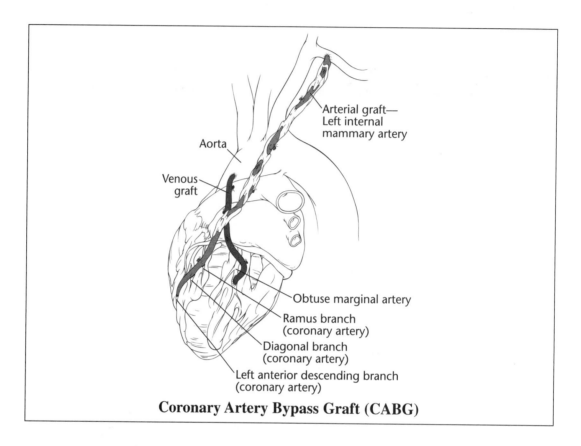

Arterial graft—
Left internal
mammary artery

Aorta

Venous
graft

Obtuse marginal artery

Ramus branch
(coronary artery)

Diagonal branch
(coronary artery)

Left anterior descending branch
(coronary artery)

**Coronary Artery Bypass Graft (CABG)**

## Exercise 4.13: Medical Terminology Review

Match the following terms with the correct definition.

1. _____ fistula           A. surgically closing off a vessel

2. _____ graft             B. blood clot

3. _____ stenosis          C. surgically made passage

4. _____ thrombus          D. piece of tissue that is transplanted surgically

5. _____ ligation          E. narrowing of a passage

## Exercise 4.14: Clinical Concepts

Fill in the blanks to the following scenarios. Choose from one of the two answers provided in parentheses.

1.  A venous access device that is inserted in the cephalic vein and the tip rests in the superior vena cava would be classified as _____ (centrally inserted, peripherally inserted).

2.  Removal of a blood clot from a vein is called a(n) _____ (atherectomy, thrombectomy).

3. A direct arteriovenous (AV) anastomosis connects the radial artery to the
_____ (cephalic vein, inferior vena cava).

4. Through a small incision in the leg, the surgeon inserts a catheter into the femoral artery. The balloon is inflated to open the artery for improved blood flow. This procedure is referred to as _____ (open transluminal balloon angioplasty, percutaneous transluminal balloon angioplasty).

5. Central venous access devices are often used on patients who require _____ (angioplasty, chemotherapy).

## Exercise 4.15: Cardiovascular System Coding Drill

Review the documentation and underline key term(s). Identify the terms used to look up the code selection in the Alphabetic Index. Assign CPT codes to the following cases. If applicable, append CPT/HCPCS Level II modifiers.

1. The surgeon repairs a ruptured aneurysm of the splenic artery.

   **Index:**_____

   **Code(s):**_____

2. Operative Note

   Diagnosis: End-stage renal disease

   Procedure: Creation of left forearm arterial venous (AV) fistula

   The patient was prepped and draped in the usual manner. An incision was made over the radial artery and cephalic vein. Each was dissected free to create an anastomosis.

   **Index:**_____

   **Code(s):**_____

3. Operative Note:

   Diagnosis: Thrombosis of right AV (Gore-Tex) graft

   Procedure: A transverse incision was made in order to complete a thrombectomy of the graft. Because the balloon catheter could not be passed, it was elected to perform an arteriotomy for removal of the thrombus. The area was irrigated, and the incision was closed.

   **Index:**_____

   > **TIP: Many experienced coders rely mainly on the Index to provide the range of codes and do not focus on locating the exact index entry.**

   **Code(s):**_____

4. A patient with a previously implanted pacing cardioverter-defibrillator now requires repositioning of the lead.

   **Index:**_____

   **Code(s):**_____

5. A surgeon performs a percutaneous transluminal angioplasty on the left femoral-popliteal artery for a patient with peripheral artery disease.

   **Index:**_____

   **Code(s):**_____

6. The patient requires a new pacemaker battery. The surgeon removes the old pacemaker generator and inserts a new dual chamber generator.

   **Index:**_____

   **Code(s):**_____

7. A surgeon performed a triple coronary artery bypass using a saphenous vein.

   **Index:**_____

   **Code(s):**_____

8. The surgeon creates a new skin pocket to relocate the pacemaker.

   **Index:**_____

   **Code(s):**_____

9. Percutaneous transcatheter placement of stent in femoral artery.

   **Index:**_____

   **Code(s):**_____

10. A surgeon performs an axillary-brachial thromboendarterectomy with patch graft.

    **Index:**_____

    **Code(s):**_____

## Exercise 4.16: Case Studies—Cardiovascular System Operative Reports

**1.**

### Operative Note

PROCEDURE: Permanent pacemaker implantation

DETAILS OF PROCEDURE: The patient was prepped and draped in the usual sterile fashion. The left subclavian vein was accessed, and the guidewire was placed in position. A deep subcutaneous pacemaker pocket was created using the blunt dissection technique. A 7 French introducer sheath was advanced over the guidewire, and the guidewire was removed. A bipolar endocardial lead model was advanced under fluoroscopic guidance and tip of pacemaker lead was positioned in the right ventricular apex.

Next, the 9.5 French introducer sheath was advanced over a separate guidewire under fluoroscopic guidance, and the guidewire was removed.

Through this sheath, a bipolar atrial screw-in lead was positioned in the right atrial appendage and the lead was screwed in.

✎ *Abstract from Documentation:*

What is the coding selection for a permanent pacemaker?

What documentation determines the correct code selection?

🕐 *Time to Code:*

**Index:**_____

**Code(s):**_____

## 2.

### Operative Report

PROCEDURE: Inferior vena cava filter placement

INDICATIONS: Massive pulmonary embolism and left lower extremity deep venous thrombosis

PROCEDURE: After informed consent was discussed, obtained, and placed on the chart, the patient was prepped and draped in the usual sterile fashion. This included all elements of maximal sterile barrier technique. 1 percent Xylocaine was used for local anesthesia. Using ultrasound guidance, the right internal jugular vein was seen to be patent and was cannulated using ultrasound guidance. A catheter was placed in the proximal common iliac venous system and inferior vena cavogram was performed. The skin tract was dilated to accommodate the delivery sheath. The inferior vena cava was deployed and follow-up venogram demonstrated the filter position within the infrarenal inferior vena cava. The delivery sheath was removed and hemostasis was obtained.

IMPRESSION: Ultrasound-guided inferior vena cavogram demonstrating normal caliber inferior vena cava with no evidence for thrombosis.

✎ *Abstract from Documentation:*

What is the intent of the procedure?

🕐 *Time to Code:*

**Index:**_____

**Code(s):**_____

## 3.

**Operative Report**

PREOPERATIVE DIAGNOSIS: Status post Port-a-Cath

POSTOPERATIVE DIAGNOSIS: Same

PROCEDURE: Removal of Port-a-Cath

INDICATIONS: The patient has completed the chemotherapy treatment and elects to remove the Port-a-Cath.

PROCEDURE: The patient was placed in supine position. Right subclavian area was prepped and adequately draped. Local anesthesia was given just over the port, and transverse incision was made. Skin incision was deepened down to port area. Fibrinous capsule was exposed and retracted and sharply dissected to remove the soft tissue. Entire fibrinous capsule was excised and then the tunnel was clamped and tied off the fibrinous capsule, after the entire system was removed. The area was irrigated. Hemostasis was assured. Subcutaneous layer was closed using 4-0. Skin was approximated using 5-0 Vicryl running stitches. Steri-Strips applied. Patient tolerated the procedure well.

*Abstract from Documentation:*

Review CPT notes preceding the coding section for central venous access procedures.

What is a Port-a-Cath?

What was the operative action?

*Time to Code:*

**Index:**_____

**Code(s):**_____

## 4.

**Operative Note**

DIAGNOSIS: Critical left main coronary artery stenosis; severe atherosclerotic disease of all native coronary arteries.

PROCEDURES PERFORMED:

1. Urgent coronary artery bypass grafting ×4 with placement of the left internal mammary artery to the left anterior descending coronary artery and placement of reverse saphenous vein grafts from the aorta to the right coronary artery, the obtuse marginal branch of the circumflex, and the diagonal branch.

2. Endoscopic harvesting of the left greater saphenous vein from left leg.

*Abstract from Documentation:*

Refer to the Coronary Artery Bypass range of procedures beginning with 33510. How are the codes organized?

How many grafts were achieved with the use of the internal mammary artery?

How many grafts were achieved with the use of the saphenous vein graft?

What guidelines pertain to reporting combined arterial-venous grafts?

🕐 *Time to Code:*

**Index:**_____

**Code(s):**_____

---

## 5.

**Operative Report**

PREOPERATIVE DIAGNOSIS: Severe right common iliac artery stenosis with claudication

POSTOPERATIVE DIAGNOSIS: Same

PROCEDURE: Angioplasty of right common iliac artery stenosis

Through a left groin incision, a 7 French Cordis introducer was placed after the lesion had been crossed with the guidewire. A 9 mm × 4 cm balloon was then chosen. The patient was given 2,000 units of heparin intra-arterially. The balloon was then positioned in the proper location and gently inflated. The stenosis dilated easily. The balloon was inflated for 1 minute and then brought down. The catheter was advanced, the guidewire removed, and completion angiography revealed satisfactory dilatation with no stenosis. The patient was taken to the recovery room in satisfactory condition.

✎ *Abstract from Documentation:*

What main procedure was performed?

What technique was used to eliminate the stenosis?

🕐 *Time to Code:*

**Index:**_____

**Code(s):**_____

# Digestive System Exercises

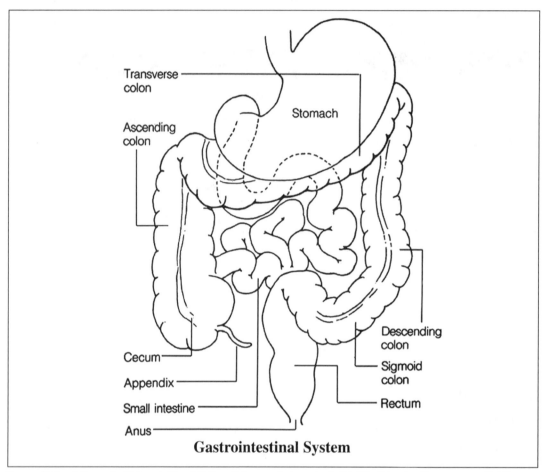

**Gastrointestinal System**

## Exercise 4.17: Crossword Puzzle

Answers are located in Appendix A.

**Across**

2. Final section of large intestine

3. Instrument to view inside body

6. Third portion of small intestines

7. Groin

**Down**

1. First part of small intestine

4. From cecum to rectum

5. Navel

## Exercise 4.18: Clinical Concepts

Fill in the blanks to the following scenarios. Choose from one of the two answers provided in parentheses.

1. The scope was introduced through the mouth and advanced to the second portion of the duodenum. Cannulation of the common bile duct was accomplished. The common bile duct and intrahepatics were normal. This operative note describes an _____ (EGD, ERCP).

2. The scope was inserted through the anus and advanced to the cecum. This procedure is described as a _____ (colonoscopy, sigmoidoscopy).

3. The physician removed part of the intestine, which required surgical connection of the two ends. This procedure is called a(n) _____ (anastomosis, fistulotomy).

4. The patient presents with a weakened area that has developed in the scarred muscle tissue around a prior abdominal surgical incision. This condition describes an _____ hernia (incisional, inguinal).

5. The patient presents with adhesions in the intestines. The physician performs an _____ to correct the condition (enteroenterostomy, enterolysis).

## Exercise 4.19: Digestive System Coding Drill

Review the documentation and underline key term(s). Identify the terms used to look up the code selection in the Alphabetic Index. Assign CPT codes to the following cases. If applicable, append CPT/HCPCS Level II modifiers.

1. Operative Note: The patient is morbidly obese with a BMI of 37. Procedure performed: Laparoscopic vertical sleeve gastrectomy.

   **Index:**_____

   **Code(s):**_____

2. Operative Note

   Diagnosis: Gallstone pancreatitis and biliary tree obstruction

   Procedure: ERCP with sphincterotomy

   Indications: The patient has gallstone pancreatitis, and an ultrasound showed a dilated common duct with stones.

   **Index:**_____

   **Code(s):**_____

3. A patient is diagnosed with papillomas of the anus. Using cryosurgery, the surgeon removes the three papillomas.

   **Index:**_____

   **Code(s):**_____

4. Procedure Performed: Partial distal gastrectomy with gastrojejunostomy

   **Index:**_____

   **Code(s):**_____

5. The patient suffered a perforation of the pharynx wall from a bottle cap. The surgeon performed a suture repair of the wound.

   **Index:**_____

   **Code(s):**_____

6. The physician performs an EGD (flexible, transoral) for removal of a coin.

   **Index:**_____

   **Code(s):**_____

7. The surgeon performed a laparoscopic repair of paraesophageal hernia.

   **Index:**_____

   **Code(s):**_____

8. The surgeon performed an excision of five external tags of the anus.

   **Index:**_____

   **Code(s):**_____

9. The surgeon performed an esophagoscopy (flexible, transoral) for removal of a polyp via hot biopsy forceps

   **Index:**_____

   **Code(s):**_____

10. Patient has the diagnosis of acute appendicitis, and the surgeon performs a laparoscopic appendectomy.

    **Index:**_____

    **Code(s):**_____

## Exercise 4.20: Case Studies—Digestive System Operative and Emergency Department Reports

**1.**

### Operative Report

PROCEDURE: Colonoscopy

INDICATIONS: Polyp seen on flexible sigmoidoscopy

PROCEDURE: After obtaining consent, the scope was passed under direct vision. Throughout the procedure, the patient's blood pressure, pulse, and oxygen saturations were monitored continuously. The Olympus pediatric flexible colonoscopy was introduced through the anus and advanced to the ileum. The colonoscopy was accomplished without difficulty. The patient tolerated the procedure well.

FINDINGS: The terminal ileum was normal. Multiple small-mouthed diverticula were found in the sigmoid colon. A pedunculated polyp was found in the sigmoid colon. The polyp was 30 mm in size. Polypectomy was performed with snare after injecting 4 cc of epinephrine in the stalk for hemostasis. Resection and retrieval were complete. Estimated blood loss was minimal.

Internal, nonbleeding, mild hemorrhoids were found.

*Abstract from Documentation:*

Was this a diagnostic or surgical colonoscopy?

What technique was used to remove the polyp?

*Time to Code:*

**Index:**_____

**Code(s):**_____

## 2.

### Operative Report

DIAGNOSIS: Esophageal stricture

PROCEDURE: Upper endoscopy with esophageal dilation

INDICATIONS FOR PROCEDURE: The patient is a 65-year-old woman who has a known esophageal stricture that has required periodic dilation in the past. She has recently had recurrent difficulty with solid food.

OPERATIVE PROCEDURE: The flexible instrument was passed easily in the mouth to the esophagus. The esophagus had normal mucosa. The gastroesophageal junction was present at 30 cm where there was a stricture present and extended for no more than a couple of millimeters in length.

There was a single linear erosion extending about 1 cm above, consistent with reflux esophagitis. Below the stricture, there was a 4 cm sliding hiatal hernia. On retroversion, no additional abnormalities were noted. The body of the stomach distended well and had a normal rugal pattern. The antrum was briefly seen and was normal, as were the duodenal bulb and descending duodenum.

The instrument was withdrawn into the stomach, and a Savary guidewire was passed under direct vision with fluoroscopic control. The instrument was withdrawn, and the patient was dilated with the passage of the 15-, 17-, and 20-mm Savary dilators with minimal resistance encountered and no heme on the dilators.

*Abstract from Documentation:*

What exactly was visualized during this endoscopic procedure?

Besides visualization (diagnostic endoscopy) what else was performed during the endoscopy?

*Time to Code:*

**Index:**_____

**Code(s):**_____

## 3.

**Emergency Department Record**

CHIEF COMPLAINT: Foreign body in throat

HISTORY OF PRESENT ILLNESS: This is a 73-year-old male who has a history of esophageal stricture, who has had multiple endoscopies to have foreign bodies removed. He was eating roast beef last night, and it stuck in his throat. He says anything he tries to eat or drink comes right back up. He called Dr. Marcus early this morning and stated that he would meet him in the emergency room. Patient denies any chest pain, fever, chills, and shortness of breath or other systemic complaints.

Dr. Marcus performed a flexible, transoral esophagoscopy and removed several pieces of meat as well as a pea. The patient did receive conscious sedation for the procedure. We watched him in the emergency room on his recovery.

IMPRESSIONS: Meat impaction in esophagus.

*Abstract from Documentation:*

What type of endoscopy was performed?

What procedure was performed during the endoscopy?

*Time to Code:*

**Index:**_____

**Code(s):**_____

## 4.

**Operative Note**

PROCEDURE: Colonoscopy with biopsy

INDICATIONS: This 26-year-old female was referred for evaluation because of abdominal pain with occasional episodes of rectal bleeding and some mucus in the stool.

PROCEDURE: The scope was inserted and advanced to the cecum. The rectum showed small pinpoint ulcers but nothing beyond that. I did take some biopsies. The sigmoid, descending, transverse, and ascending colon were normal.

*Abstract from Documentation:*

What was performed during this procedure?

*Time to Code:*

**Index:**_____

**Code(s):**_____

**5.**

## Operative Report

PREOPERATIVE DIAGNOSIS: Thrombosed hemorrhoids

POSTOPERATIVE DIAGNOSIS: Same

INDICATIONS: This 25-year-old female, one week postpartum, complains of extremely painful hemorrhoids. Examination revealed circumferential prolapsed hemorrhoids with partial thrombosis in multiple areas.

PROCEDURE: After induction of general anesthesia, she was prepped and draped in the usual sterile fashion. The patient was placed in lithotomy position, and a retractor was placed in the anus. Very prominent, large, partially thrombosed external hemorrhoid was identified at 7–8 o'clock in the lithotomy position. It was grasped with a hemorrhoidal clamp. A 2-0 chromic stitch was placed at the apex. The Bovie electrocautery was then used to elliptically excise the large hemorrhoid, staying superficial to the sphincter muscle. Bleeding was controlled with Bovie electrocautery. The mucosa was closed with a running chromic stitch, leaving the end-point epidermis open.

Two other very large external hemorrhoids with thrombosis were then identified, at the 5 o'clock position in lithotomy and at the 10–11 o'clock position. These two hemorrhoids were excised in the exact same fashion as the first hemorrhoid. At the conclusion, there was no evidence of bleeding. The patient was returned to the recovery area in good condition.

*Abstract from Documentation:*

What method was used to remove the hemorrhoids?

Were the hemorrhoids internal or external?

How many columns or groups were documented?

*Time to Code:*

**Index:**_____

**Code(s):**_____

**6.**

## Operative Report

PREOPERATIVE DIAGNOSIS: Inadequate p.o. intake

POSTOPERATIVE DIAGNOSIS: Same

OPERATION: Percutaneous endoscopic gastrostomy tube placement

ANESTHESIA: IV sedation

CLINICAL HISTORY: The patient is a 75-year-old female patient with inadequate p.o. intake who presents now for PEG tube placement.

OPERATIVE PROCEDURE: After establishment of an adequate level of IV sedation and viscous spray of the oropharynx, EGD scope was inserted without difficulty to the second portion of the duodenum from whence it was gradually withdrawn. There were no striking duodenal findings. The pylorus appeared unremarkable and on visualization, the antrum, body, and fundus of the stomach were also unremarkable. With withdrawal of the scope, the esophagus and GE junction visualized normal. Insufflation of the stomach was undertaken and at point of maximal transillumination in the epigastrium, local infiltration was undertaken by Dr. June and a slit incision was made. Needle within a cannula was then threaded percutaneously directly into the stomach under visualization. Inner cannula was removed, and guidewire was passed. Loop forceps were then passed endoscopically and guidewire was grasped in the stomach and brought out orally, whence it was anchored to a PEG tube that was pulled to emanate via the anterior abdominal wall, being anchored to appropriate position.

The patient tolerated the procedure well. There were no complications.

*Abstract from Documentation:*

What is a PEG tube?

How was the PEG tube inserted?

*Time to Code:*

**Index:**_____

**Code(s):**_____

## 7.

### Operative Report

PREOPERATIVE DIAGNOSIS: Right colon cancer; probable liver metastasis

POSTOPERATIVE DIAGNOSIS: Cecal cancer, extensive bilateral liver metastasis

PROCEDURES PERFORMED: Right colectomy and biopsy of right lobe liver nodule

INDICATIONS: Patient is a 67-year-old man who presented with anemia. Colonoscopy demonstrated bleeding cecal carcinoma. CT scan suggested liver metastasis. He presents now for a palliative right colectomy and biopsy of liver nodule.

DESCRIPTION: The patient was brought to the operating room and placed in a supine position. Satisfactory general endotracheal anesthesia was achieved. He was prepped and draped, exposing the anterior abdomen, and a lower midline incision was created sharply through subcutaneous tissues by electrocautery. Linea Alba was parted, and exploration was performed. The right colon was mobilized by dissection in the avascular plane. The patient had a 3–4 cm cecal cancer. The right ureter was identified and preserved.

The terminal ileum and distal ascending colon were divided with GIA-60 stapling devices. The right colic artery and lymph node tissue were resected back to the origin of the superior mesenteric artery with clamps and 3-0 silk ties. The specimen was forwarded to pathology. A stapled functional end-to-end anastomosis was then performed. The antimesenteric edges were reapproximated with a single fire of GIA-60 stapler. The defect created by the stapler was then closed with interrupted 3-0 silk Lembert sutures. The mesocolon was reapproximated with some interrupted 3-0 silk sutures. Hemostasis was confirmed. The right anterior liver nodule was biopsied with a Tru-Cut needle. Hemostasis was achieved. The midline fascia was closed with running 1-0 Prolene suture. The skin was approximated with staples. The wound was dressed. The procedure was concluded. The patient tolerated the procedure well and was taken to recovery in stable condition. Estimated blood loss was less than 100 cc. There were no complications.

### Pathology Report

#1-RIGHT HEMICOLECTOMY: Adenocarcinoma of cecum

#2-LIVER BIOPSIES: Metastatic adenocarcinoma

✎ *Abstract from Documentation:*

Locate the code selection for colectomy. What additional information is needed from the operative report to assign a correct code?

In the index, what code selection is provided for the liver biopsy?

How are the codes differentiated?

🕐 *Time to Code:*

**Index:**_____

**Code(s):**_____

## 8.

### Operative Report

PREOPERATIVE DIAGNOSIS: Left inguinal hernia

POSTOPERATIVE DIAGNOSIS: Left inguinal hernia

PROCEDURE: Left inguinal hernia repair

INDICATIONS FOR SURGERY: The patient is a 62-year-old male who was referred to the Surgical Outpatient Office for evaluation of a reducible left groin bulge. Physical examination disclosed the presence of a reducible left inguinal hernia. No previous history of hernia repairs. The patient was scheduled for an elective repair.

OPERATION: The patient was brought to the operating room and placed on the operating table in supine position. Pneumatic compression TED hose was applied to the patient's legs. Following induction of a suitable level of general endotracheal anesthesia, the patient's lower abdomen and groin were prepped and draped in a sterile fashion. The patient's left groin was entered through a 7 cm curvilinear incision made one fingerbreadth above the parallel to the left inguinal ligament. The skin and subcutaneous tissues were divided down to the level of the external oblique aponeurosis. Tributaries to the saphenous vein, which were encountered during this portion of the resection, were individually ligated and divided. Dissection along the patient's external oblique aponeurosis revealed the patient's external inguinal ring. Subcutaneous tissues were cleared from the external ring. The ilioinguinal nerve was identified exiting from the external ring and traced on to the subcutaneous tissues.

The external oblique aponeurosis was opened from the external ring in the direction of its fibers laterally over a distance of approximately 7 cm. Care was taken during this portion of the dissection to avoid injury to the underlying ilioinguinal nerve, which had been previously visualized. Superior and inferior flaps of the aponeurosis were elevated. The ilioinguinal nerve was traced in a retrograde fashion back to the point where it exited from the internal oblique muscle. It was reflected inferiorly to avoid injury during the remainder of the dissection.

The patient's spermatic cord was dissected free from surrounding tissues at the level of the pubic tubercle and encircled with a Penrose drain. Lateral fraction on the spermatic cord revealed the patient's direct space, which revealed some laxity, but no hernia formation.

A longitudinal incision was made in the cremasteric and the lobe surrounding the spermatic cord. Dissection within this spermatic cord revealed an indirect inguinal hernia sac. The sac was dissected free from the associated cord structure back to the level of the internal inguinal ring. It could be reduced back inside of the abdominal cavity at this point.

The preperitoneal space behind the transversalis fascia was opened with finger and sponge dissection over the entire inguinal floor. During this dissection, the epigastric vessels were elevated against the abdominal wall and the preperitoneal tissues were pushed backward from there. After ensuring wide dissection of the epreperitoneal space, an extended Prolene Hernia System manufactured by Ethicon was inserted into the preperitoneal space. The preperitoneal patch portion of this system was ensuring deployment of the preperitoneal portion of the mesh; the anterior flap of the hernia system was deployed on the inguinal floor. The anterior portion of the mesh was secured to the pubic tubercle and conjoined tendon using #2-0 Vicryl sutures. A slit was cut on the inferior edge of the anterior flap, and this was approximately 6 cm from the pubic tubercle to accommodate the spermatic cord. The spermatic cord and the patient's left ilioinguinal nerve were brought through this slit. The slit was then closed with a single #2-0 Vicryl suture. Care was taken to make certain that there was no vascular compromise of the spermatic cord when the slit was closed.

The lateral aspect of the anterior flap was deployed against the muscular portion of the internal oblique muscle over a distance of approximately 6 cm lateral to the spermatic cord.

The ilioinguinal nerve was injected with 0.5 percent Marcaine at the point where it exited the internal oblique muscle. 2–3 cc of 0.5 percent Marcaine was then injected into the spermatic cord for the postoperative analgesia. The skin surrounding the incision was also infiltrated with 0.5 percent Marcaine for postoperative analgesia.

The wound was examined for hemostasis, which was felt to be complete. The external oblique aponeurosis was repaired using interrupted #2-0 Vicryl sutures. Scarpa's fascia was closed using interrupted #3-0 Vicryl sutures. The skin was closed using a running subcuticular #4-0 Monocryl suture. The wound was washed, dried, and Steri-Strips and sterile dressing were applied. The patient's left testicle was pulled back to its native position in the left hemiscrotum. Patient was permitted to emerge from general anesthesia, was extubated, and transported to the recovery room in stable condition.

✎ *Abstract from Documentation:*

Refer to the range of hernia repair codes. What documentation is needed before the code is selected?

Did the repair include implantation of mesh?

🕐 *Time to Code:*

**Index:**_____

**Code(s):**_____

# Chapter 4
# Surgery: Part II

# Urinary System Exercises

Answers to the exercises in this section will not apply modifier 51 (multiple procedures) or sequencing for claims submission. The focus of these exercises is to practice accurate assignment of CPT codes without regard to payer guidelines. The answers will include use of lateral modifiers, such as RT, FA, and Modifier 50 for bilateral. For the purposes of instruction, this book uses a dash to separate each five-character CPT code from its two-character modifier. However, dashes are not used in actual code assignments and reimbursement claims.

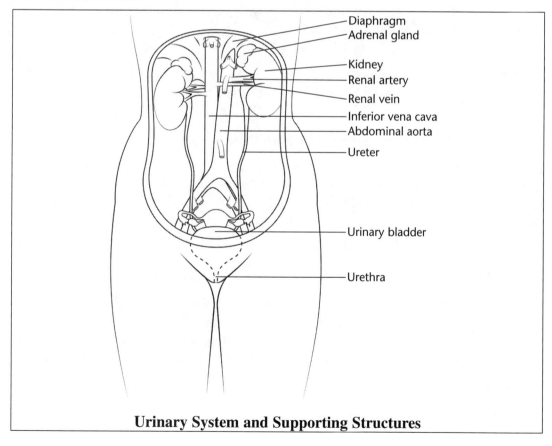

**Urinary System and Supporting Structures**

## Exercise 4.21: Medical Terminology Review

Match the medical terms with the correct definitions.

1. ____ -lith          A. sac that stores urine

2. ____ ureter        B. duct that leads urine out of body from bladder

3. ____ bladder       C. duct from kidney to bladder

4. ____ kidney        D. stone

5. ____ urethra       E. organ that purifies blood and excretes waste in urine

## Exercise 4.22: Clinical Concepts

Fill in the blanks for the following scenarios. Choose from one of the two answers provided in parentheses.

1. Which of the following procedures would use sound waves to break up a ureteral stone?_____ (lithotripsy, cystopexy)

2. Which of the following procedures would be performed to treat ureteral stenosis? _____ (insertion of ureteral stent, transurethral resection)

3. The surgeon inserts a telescope-like tube into the bladder from the natural orifice to visualize the lower urinary tract. This procedure is referred to as a(n) _____ (cystourethroscopy, ERCP).

4. The surgeon removed urinary stones through an incision directly into the body of the kidney. This procedure is known as a(n) _____ (ureterectomy, nephrolithotomy).

5. Which of the following procedures would be performed for urinary stress incontinence? _____ (urethral suspension, cystorrhaphy)

## Exercise 4.23: Urinary System Coding Drill

For all coding exercises, review the documentation and underline key term(s). Identify the terms used to look up the code selection in the Alphabetic Index. Assign CPT codes to the following cases. If applicable, append CPT/HCPCS Level II modifiers. In some cases, the student will be prompted to answer questions about the case study.

1. The surgeon performs a laparoscopic ablation of a renal cyst.

   **Index:**_____

   **Code(s):** _____

2. Operative Note: Cystoscopy to remove small stones from the patient's upper right ureter and another stone lodged in the middle left ureter. Both stones were manipulated back into the kidney with subsequent placement of double J ureteral stents in each ureter.

   **Index:**_____

   **Code(s):** _____

3. Operative Note: Patient has a ureteral stricture. Performed a cystoscopy with ureteroscopy and laser treatment of the stricture.

   **Index:** _____

   **Code(s):** _____

4. Operative Note: Performed a cystoscopy with resection of a 4.0-cm bladder tumor. The procedure concluded with a steroid injection into the urethral stricture.

   **Index:** _____

   **Code(s):** _____

5. The surgeon aspirates the cyst of the kidney with the use of a percutaneous needle.

   **Index:** _____

   **Code(s):** _____

6. The surgeon performs a laparoscopic nephrectomy with partial ureterectomy.

   **Index:** _____

   **Code(s):** _____

7. Percutaneous nephrostolithotomy for basket extraction of 1.5 cm stone

   **Index:** _____

   **Code(s):** _____

8. Under direct visualization, the surgeon performs a drainage ureterotomy.

   **Index:** _____

   **Code(s):** _____

9. Percutaneous needle biopsy of the kidney

   **Index:** _____

   **Code(s):** _____

10. The surgeon performed a cystoscopy with ureteroscopy for laser treatment of a stricture of the ureteropelvic junction.

   **Index:** _____

   **Code(s):** _____

## Exercise 4.24: Case Studies—Urinary System Operative Reports

**1.**

### Operative Report

PREOPERATIVE DIAGNOSES:
1. Interstitial cystitis
2. Urethral stenosis

POSTOPERATIVE DIAGNOSES:
1. Interstitial cystitis
2. Urethral stenosis

OPERATIONS PERFORMED:
1. Cystoscopy
2. Urethral dilation

OPERATIVE FINDINGS: Urethra was tight at 26 French and dilated with 32 French. Bladder neck is normal. Ureteral orifice is normal size, shape, and position, effluxing clear bilaterally. Bladder mucosa is normal. Bladder capacity is 700 mL under anesthesia. There is moderate glomerulation consistent with interstitial cystitis. Residual urine was 150 mL.

INDICATIONS: A patient with severe symptoms.

DESCRIPTION OF OPERATION: The patient was brought to the cystoscopy suite and placed on the table in lithotomy position. The patient was prepped and draped in the usual sterile fashion. A 21 Olympus cystoscope was inserted, and the bladder was viewed with 12- and 70-degree lenses. Bladder was filled by gravity to capacity, emptied, and again cystoscopy was performed with findings as above. Urethra was then calibrated with 32 French and dilation performed. The patient was taken to the recovery room in stable condition.

*Abstract from Documentation:*

What is meant by the "urethra was then calibrated"?

*Time to Code:*

**Index:** _____

**Code(s):** _____

**2.**

### Operative Report

PREOPERATIVE DIAGNOSIS: Detrusor hyperreflexia

POSTOPERATIVE DIAGNOSIS: Same

PROCEDURE PERFORMED: Cystoscopy with injection of Botox in the floor of the bladder

INDICATIONS: The patient presents with severe detrusor hyperreflexia resulting in urgency and urge incontinence. This lady previously has undergone a Marshall-Marchetti-Krantz bladder neck suspension, which brought about complete relief of her stress incontinence. She recently has developed detrusor hyperreflexia with urge incontinence. She has failed anticholinergic medication treatment for this problem. She is brought to the operating room for Botox injection in the floor of the bladder.

PROCEDURE: The patient was placed in the lithotomy position and prepped and draped in the usual manner. She was administered Versed and Stadol intravenously for sedation. A 22 French cystoscope sheath was introduced into the bladder over an obturator. One hundred units of Botox A were injected into the floor of the bladder. The Botox was dissolved in 10 mL of preservative-free saline, and there were 10 injection sites with 1 mL containing 10 units of Botox at 10 sites across the floor of the bladder immediately above the trigone. The bladder was drained, and the cystoscope was withdrawn. The patient tolerated the procedure well and left the operating room in good condition. The patient has been placed on Cipro 250 mg 1 tablet every 12 hours #6 prophylaxis for infection following instrumentation.

*Abstract from Documentation:*

What is the purpose of injecting the bladder with Botox?

Scan the CPT coding options for injecting the bladder during a cystourethroscopy procedure, record your findings.

*Time to Code:*

**Index:** _____

**Code(s):** _____

## 3.

### Operative Report

PREOPERATIVE DIAGNOSIS: A 6-mm stone in the left lower pole

POSTOPERATIVE DIAGNOSIS: A 6-mm stone in the left lower pole

OPERATION PERFORMED: Left extracorporeal shock wave lithotripsy (ESWL)

ANESTHESIA: Intravenous sedation

INDICATIONS FOR PROCEDURE: This is a 57-year-old man who has been known to have a stone in the left upper pole for a number of years. He recently presented with left renal colic. An x-ray showed the stone to have migrated into the proximal ureter. Recently, he underwent cystoscopy, the stone was successfully flushed into the kidney, and a double-J stent was placed. He now needs to be treated with ESWL.

DESCRIPTION OF PROCEDURE: The patient was placed onto the treatment table, and, after the administration of intravenous sedation, he was positioned over the shock wave electrode. The x-ray showed the stone to now be located in the lower pole of the left kidney. Biaxial fluoroscopy was utilized to position the stone at the focal point of the shock wave generator. The stone was initially treated at 17 kV, increasing up to 24 kV. The stone was treated with 3,000 shocks. Throughout the procedure, fluoroscopic manipulations and adjustments were made in order to maintain the stone in the focal point of the shock wave generator. At the conclusion of the procedure, the stone appeared to have fragmented nicely, and the patient was placed on a stretcher and taken to the recovery room in good condition.

*Abstract from Documentation:*

How were the stones removed?

*Time to Code:*

**Index:** _____

**Code(s):** _____

## 4.

### Operative Report

PREOPERATIVE DIAGNOSIS: Multiple bladder stones

PROCEDURE: Cystoscopy with cystolitholapaxy

INDICATIONS: This 58-year-old patient was found to have several bladder stones. He is here today for removal of those stones. The patient is voiding well currently. Informed consent was signed, and risks and benefits were explained and understood by the patient prior to the procedure. He agreed to proceed.

DESCRIPTION OF PROCEDURE: The patient was taken to the cystoscopy suite and placed in dorsal lithotomy position after adequate induction of general anesthesia. Levaquin 500 mg was given intravenously, preoperatively. Perineum and genitalia were prepped and draped in the usual sterile fashion. A 21 French cystourethroscope was inserted into the urethra, and the prostate was visualized. He did have some lateral lobe hyperplasia of the prostate, but otherwise no significant pathology in the urethra. The bladder was then entered and drained. Multiple bladder stones were seen, and these were all less than half a centimeter apiece. The bladder stones were evacuated using cystoscope and irrigation with the Ellik evacuator. All stones were removed without difficulty. After the bladder was drained and all of the stones removed, the patient was awakened. He returned to the recovery room in satisfactory condition.

✎ *Abstract from Documentation:*

During the cystoscopy, from which location were stones removed?

🕐 *Time to Code:*

**Index:** _____

**Code(s):** _____

## 5.

### Operative Report

PREOPERATIVE DIAGNOSIS: History of low-grade transitional cell carcinoma

POSTOPERATIVE DIAGNOSIS: Same

PROCEDURE: Flexible cystoscopy

INDICATIONS: Patient is a 49-year-old male diagnosed with low-grade transitional cell carcinoma of the bladder. He is here today for his regular bladder tumor follow-up.

DETAILS: Patient's genitalia were prepped and draped in the typical fashion. 20 cc of 2 percent lidocaine jelly was instilled into the urethra. The anesthesia was given five minutes to set in. The #19 French flexible cystoscope was passed through the urethra into the bladder. Once inside the bladder, the entire bladder mucosa was evaluated. No lesions were identified. Both ureteral orifices were seen and were found to be normal. At this point, the scope was removed. Patient will be called in 3 months for his next follow-up.

✎ *Abstract from Documentation:*

What was visualized during the endoscopy procedure?

🕐 *Time to Code:*

**Index:** _____

**Code(s):** _____

# Male Genital System Exercises

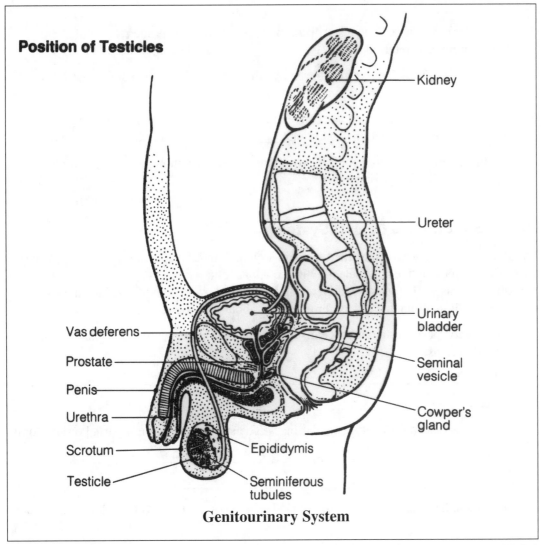

**Position of Testicles**

Kidney

Ureter

Urinary bladder

Seminal vesicle

Cowper's gland

Vas deferens

Prostate

Penis

Urethra

Scrotum

Testicle

Epididymis

Seminiferous tubules

**Genitourinary System**

Source: National Cancer Institute. n.d. VisualsOnline. Unknown photographer/artist. http://visualsonline.cancer.gov/details.cfm?imageid=1782.

## Exercise 4.25: Medical Terminology Review

Match the medical terms with the definitions.

1. ____ epididymis     A. organ that produces sperm

2. ____ vas deferens     B. surgical removal of one or both testicles

3. ____ testicles     C. duct that conveys sperm from testicles to urethra

4. ____ orchiectomy     D. surgical removal of foreskin

5. ____ circumcision     E. duct along which sperm passes to vas deferens

## Exercise 4.26: Clinical Concepts

Fill in the blanks for the following scenarios. Choose from one of the two answers provided in parentheses.

1.  The male patient is seeking a sterilization procedure to prevent the release of sperm. This procedure is referred to as _____ (orchiectomy, vasectomy).

2.  The surgeon uses a clamp device to remove the prepuce. This procedure is known as a _____ (circumcision, vasectomy).

3.  A patient has been diagnosed with undescended testis. Which of the following procedures would correct this condition? _____ (urethroplasty, orchiopexy)

4.  What is the most common surgical procedure to treat benign prostatic hypertrophy? _____ (TURP, prostatotomy)

## Exercise 4.27: Male Genital System Coding Drill

For all coding exercises, review the documentation and underline key term(s). Identify the terms used to look up the code selection in the Alphabetic Index. Assign CPT codes to the following cases. If applicable, append CPT/HCPCS Level II modifiers. In some cases, the student will be prompted to answer questions about the case study.

1.  The surgeon performs a one-stage distal hypospadias repair with urethroplasty using local skin flaps.

    **Index:**_____

    **Code(s):** _____

2.  The patient is seen for a left testicular mass. The surgeon performs a partial orchiectomy.

    **Index:**_____

    **Code(s):** _____

3.  The patient has a history of azoospermia. The surgeon performs bilateral open testicular biopsies.

    **Index:**_____

    **Code(s):** _____

4.  With the use of a laser, the surgeon removes a papilloma from the patient's penis.

    **Index:**_____

    **Code(s):** _____

5.  Patient is a 55-year-old male with a Mentor inflatable three-piece penile prosthesis that had been causing problems. He was experiencing issues with prolonged erections while deflating the prosthesis. It was elected to remove the prosthesis and insert a Duraphase II penile prosthesis. There was some evidence of infection in the area, which was irrigated.

    **Index:**_____

    **Code(s):** _____

## Exercise 4.28: Case Studies—Male Genital System Operative Reports

**1.**

### Operative Report

PREOPERATIVE DIAGNOSIS: T2C, NX, M0 prostate cancer

POSTOPERATIVE DIAGNOSIS: T2C, NX, M0 prostate cancer

OPERATION: Radical retropubic prostatectomy with bilateral pelvic lymph node dissection

INDICATIONS: This 62-year-old man had an elevated PSA of 12.5 on routine screening. He recently underwent a transrectal ultrasound and biopsy that revealed approximately 9 out of 10 cores positive for adenocarcinoma of the prostate. With hormonal therapy, his PSA preoperatively had decreased to 0.1 on androgen blockade.

PROCEDURE: After administration of general anesthesia, the patient was placed in supine position, prepped, and draped in the usual sterile fashion. A midline incision was made to the left of the umbilicus and carried down to the public bone. The fascia was split in the midline, as well as the rectus muscle, and the retropubic space was then entered. Each obturator fossa was delineated using blunt dissection. A fixed Balfour retractor was then placed.

A left pelvic lymph node dissection was then performed in the usual fashion. Care was taken to preserve the obturator nerve. It was noted that there were no grossly enlarged nodes in the area. Clips were used to control bleeding and lymph drainage.

A similar dissection was performed on the right side with no damage to the obturator nerve, and there were no grossly enlarged lymph nodes.

Frozen section analysis did not reveal any adenocarcinoma.

The endopelvic fascia was then identified and defatted. It was split along its lateral borders from the puboprostatic ligaments and down to the bladder neck. The dorsal vein complex and endopelvic fascia were then gathered using a curved Babcock clamp. Two 0 Vicryl suture ligatures were placed at the bladder neck to control bleeding.

A clamp was then passed between the anterior urethra and dorsal vein complex, and a 0 Vicryl suture was then tied around this complex. A second 0 Vicryl suture ligature was also placed in the most distal portion. The dorsal vein complex was divided using electrocautery, and excellent hemostasis was noted. The prostatic apex was identified with further sharp and blunt dissection.

The anterior half of the urethra was divided sharply using the #15 blade. Next, the Foley catheter was passed into the wound and divided. The posterior urethra was then sharply transected in a similar fashion. The catheter was used to provide some subtle traction of the prostate. The rectourethralis was taken down using a right-angle clamp and electrocautery. Each neurovascular bundle was also tied and ligated.

The prostate could be mobilized up to the bladder neck.

The lateral pedicles were controlled using 2-0 Vicryl sutures and divided. A small horizontal incision was then made over the seminal vesicles and ampulla of the vas. Each of these structures was then dissected out using sharp and blunt dissection. Clips were used to control bleeding. The seminal vesicles could be removed in their entirety. Each vas was clipped and ligated.

An anatomic bladder-neck-preserving dissection was then performed, and the prostate was sharply transected off the bladder neck. The bladder mucosa was everted using a running 4-0 Monocryl suture. 2-0 Vicryl sutures were placed at the 6 o'clock position to tighten the bladder neck to 20 French.

Four 2-0 Monocryl sutures were placed in this bladder neck at equally spaced distances. A Greenwald sound was then placed into the distal urethral stump, and the corresponding bladder neck sutures were then placed into the urethral stump under direct visualization.

The bladder neck was then brought down to the urethral stump using a curved Babcock clamp. All bleeding was controlled, and the wound was irrigated with normal saline. The anastomosis was then tied down and, upon testing, was shown to be watertight.

Two Jackson-Pratt drains were then brought out through each lower abdominal quadrant in a separate stab-wound incision. They were used to drain each obturator fossa and around the anastomosis. The fascia was reapproximated using interrupted #1 figure-of-eight Vicryl sutures. The subcutaneous tissue was closed with a running 2-0 chromic suture. The skin was reapproximated using staples. Each drain was sutured in with a 2-0 silk suture. The patient tolerated the procedure well and was discharged to the recovery room in stable condition.

## Abstract from Documentation:

Review the Alphabetic Index for the coding selection for Prostatectomy. What documentation would be needed to choose the range to verify?

## Time to Code:

**Index:** _____

**Code(s):** _____

## 2.

### Operative Report

PROCEDURE: Circumcision

ANESTHESIA: Regional

DESCRIPTION OF PROCEDURE: The newborn patient was cleaned and draped in sterile fashion and was first numbed at the base of the penis with 1 percent lidocaine without epinephrine, after which time it was noted that the meatus was at the tip of the penis. The dorsum of the foreskin was then clamped and an incision was made along the clamp line. The foreskin was then retracted; Gomco bell, size #2, was placed over the tip of the penis, and the foreskin was retracted over the bell and secured with a safety pin. The clamp was then placed and secured. It was held for approximately 5 minutes until appropriate blanching was obtained. The foreskin was then removed with a #11 blade. The Gomco bell and clamp were then removed. There was minimal bleeding. The patient was then dressed with a sterile Vaseline gauze, and the Betadine was also cleaned from the area. He was returned to the newborn nursery, fairly quiet, for observation. The mother was spoken with after the procedure and told that the patient tolerated it well, and she was satisfied.

## Abstract from Documentation:

Refer to Circumcision in the Alphabetic Index. What information do you need from the operative report to begin your coding assignment selection process?

## Time to Code:

**Index:** _____

**Code(s):** _____

## 3.

### Operative Report

PREOPERATIVE DIAGNOSIS: Elevated prostate-specific antigen

POSTOPERATIVE DIAGNOSIS: Same

PROCEDURE PERFORMED: Ultrasound-guided prostate needle biopsy

ANESTHESIA: General anesthesia

COMPLICATIONS: None

SPECIMENS REMOVED: 12 core needle biopsies of the prostate

INDICATIONS: The patient is a 57-year-old man. He was found on recent labs to have an elevated PSA at the level of 4.5. He has therefore consented to prostate needle biopsy.

DETAILS OF PROCEDURES: Patient was brought back to the Cysto Suite and moved into the lateral decubitus position. After smooth induction of general anesthesia, a digital rectal exam was performed. There were no nodules palpated. The prostate was smooth, firm, and benign feeling. The ultrasound probe was then inserted into the rectum. There were no abnormalities seen on ultrasound. We then proceeded to take a total of 12 core needle specimens of the prostate, two from the right base, two from the right mid, two from the right apex, followed by two from the left base, two from left mid, and two from the left apex. The patent tolerated the procedure well. There was minimal blood loss. Patient was transferred back to the Post-anesthesia Care Unit in stable condition. He will be sent home with three days of antibiotics, and we will follow up on his pathology.

*Abstract from Documentation:*

What technique was used to obtain the biopsy?

*Time to Code:*

**Index:** _____

**Code(s):** _____

## 4.

### Operative Report

PREOPERATIVE DIAGNOSIS: Left hydrocele

POSTOPERATIVE DIAGNOSIS: Same

OPERATION PERFORMED: Left hydrocelectomy

INDICATIONS: This 55-year-old male with a history of left hydrocele swelling causing discomfort requesting intervention after evaluation and preoperative consultation.

OPERATION: Patient was sterilely prepped and draped in the usual fashion. A transverse incision across the left hemiscrotum was made approximately 4 cm in length down to the level of the hydrocele. Hydrocele was removed from the incision and stripped of its fibrous attachments. Hydrocele was opened and drained. The excess sac was removed and discarded. The sac was then everted with the testicle, and a running #2-0 chromic stitch in a locking fashion was placed across the edges of the sac. Meticulous hemostasis was achieved. The testicle and spermatic cord were then replaced back to the patient's left scrotum. There was no damage done to the vas deferens. The dartos layer was reapproximated using #2-0 running locking chromic stitch. The skin was closed in a running horizontal mattress fashion using #3-0 chromic. The patient tolerated the procedure well.

*Abstract from Documentation:*

Locate Hydrocele in the Alphabetic Index. What documentation from the operative report is needed to accurately assign codes?

*Time to Code:*

**Index:** _____

**Code(s):** _____

# Female Genital System Exercises

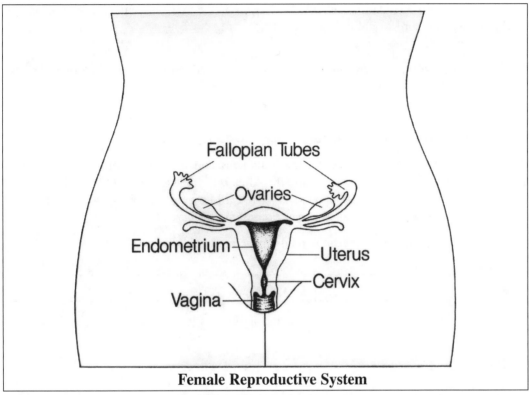

**Female Reproductive System**

Source: National Cancer Institute. n.d. VisualsOnline. Unknown photographer/artist. http://visualsonline.cancer.gov/details.cfm? imageid=1783.

## Exercise 4.29: Medical Terminology Review

Match the following medical terms with the correct definition.

1. ____ cervix
    A. surgical procedure; instrument inserted into abdominal wall to view internal organs

2. ____ vagina
    B. produces eggs

3. ____ ovary
    C. tube leading from genitalia to cervix

4. ____ colposcopy
    D. passage forming lower end of uterus

5. ____ laparoscopy
    E. surgical procedure to examine vagina and cervix

## Exercise 4.30: Clinical Concepts

Fill in the blanks for the following scenarios.

1. As a result of a positive Pap smear, the surgeon recommends a _____ to determine the cause (laparoscopy, colposcopy).

2. A surgeon removes both ovaries. This procedure is referred to as a(n) _____ (omentectomy, oophorectomy).

3. The surgeon excised extensive adhesions that encased the ovary. Freeing of adhesions is known as _____ (ligation, lysis).

4. The surgeon reports that the patient has a lesion on the external genitalia. Documentation in the health record would indicate that it was a(n) _____ lesion (vulvar, endocervical).

5. Which of the following procedures would be associated with removal of uterine fibroids? _____ (myomectomy, cerclage of uterine cervix)

## Exercise 4.31: Female Genital System Coding Drill

For all coding exercises, review the documentation and underline key term(s). Identify the terms used to look up the code selection in the Alphabetic Index. Assign CPT codes to the following cases. If applicable, append CPT/HCPCS Level II modifiers. In some cases, the student will be prompted to answer questions about the case study.

1. The surgeon performs an incision and drainage of vulvar abscess.

    **Index:**_____

    **Code(s):** _____

2. The surgeon inserts a scope into the vagina and passes it to the uterus where a biopsy of the endometrium was performed.

    **Index:**_____

    **Code(s):** _____

3. Operative Note: Patient has chronic complaints of right pelvic pain. Taken to OR for a laparoscopy. Inspection into the pelvis revealed multiple adhesions attached to the left tube and ovary. These adhesions were lysed bluntly with probe. No other abnormalities noted.

    **Index:**_____

    **Code(s):** _____

4. Operative Note: Patient treated for a 2.5 cm lesion of vagina. The lesion was lasered and hemostasis obtained for bleeding.

    **Index:**_____

    **Code(s):** _____

5. The OB/GYN physician delivers a baby via Cesarean section. The physician has provided all obstetrical care prior to delivery and will continue to follow the patient for her postpartum care.

    What coding guidelines pertain to maternity care and are applicable in this case?

    **Index:**_____

    **Code(s):** _____

# Exercise 4.32: Case Studies—Female Genital System Operative Reports

## 1.

**Operative Report**

PREOPERATIVE DIAGNOSIS: Uterine fibroids

POSTOPERATIVE DIAGNOSIS: Multiple uterine fibroids, uterus 250 g, 2 cm right ovarian cyst

PROCEDURE: Laparoscopic-assisted vaginal hysterectomy with bilateral salpingo-oophorectomy

PROCEDURE IN DETAIL: The patient was taken to the operating room and placed in the supine position. After adequate general anesthesia had been obtained, the patient was prepped and draped in the usual fashion for laparoscopic-assisted vaginal hysterectomy. The bladder was drained. A small infraumbilical skin incision was made with the scalpel, and 10-mm laparoscopic sleeve and trocar were introduced without difficulty. The trocar was removed. The laparoscope was placed and 2 L of $CO_2$ gas was insufflated in the patient's abdomen.

A second incision was made suprapubically and a 12-mm laparoscopic sleeve and trocar were introduced under direct visualization. A 5-mm laparoscopic sleeve and trocar were placed in the left lower quadrant under direct visualization. A manipulator was used to examine the patient's pelvic organs.

There was a small cyst on the right ovary. Both ovaries were free from adhesions. The ureters were free from the operative field. After measuring the ovarian distal pedicles, the endo-GIA staple was placed across each round ligament.

At this time, attention was turned to the vaginal part of the procedure. A weighted speculum was placed in the vagina. The anterior lip of the cervix was grasped with a Lahey tenaculum. Posterior colpotomy incision was made and the posterior peritoneum entered in this fashion. The uterosacral ligaments were bilaterally clamped, cut, and Heaney sutured with #1 chromic. The cardinal ligaments were bilaterally clamped, cut, and ligated. The anterior vaginal mucosa was then incised with the scalpel, and with sharp and blunt dissection, the bladder was freed from the underlying cervix. The bladder pillars were bilaterally clamped, cut, and ligated. The uterine vessels were then bilaterally clamped, cut, and ligated. Visualization was difficult because the patient had a very narrow pelvic outlet. In addition, several small fibroids made placement of clamps somewhat difficult. Using the clamp, cut, and tie method after the anterior peritoneum had been entered with scissors, the uterus was then left without vascular supply. The fundus was delivered by flipping the uterus posteriorly, and through an avascular small pedicle, Heaney clamps were placed across, and the uterus was then removed en bloc with the tubes and ovaries attached.

At this point, the remaining Heaney pedicles were ligated with a free-hand suture of 0 chromic. Sponge and instrument counts were correct. Avascular pedicles were inspected and found to be hemostatic. The posterior vaginal cuff was then closed using running interlocking suture of #1 chromic. The anterior peritoneum was then grasped, and using pursestring suture of 0 chromic, the peritoneum was closed. The vaginal cuff was then closed reincorporating the previously tagged uterosacral ligaments into the vaginal cuff through the anterior and posterior vaginal cuff. Another figure-of-eight suture totally closed the cuff. Hemostasis was excellent. Foley was then placed in the patient's bladder, and clear urine was noted to be draining. At this point, the laparoscope was placed back through the 10-mm sleeve and the vaginal cuff inspected. A small amount of old blood was suctioned away, but all areas were hemostatic.

The laparoscopic instruments were removed after the excess gas had been allowed to escape. The incisions were closed first with suture of 2-0 Vicryl through the fascia of each incision, and then the skin edges were reapproximated with interrupted sutures of 3-0 plain. Sponge and instrument counts were correct. The patient was awakened from general anesthesia and taken to the recovery room in stable condition.

✎ *Abstract from Documentation:*

Refer to the key term Hysterectomy in the Alphabetic Index. What key documentation is needed to lead to the correct coding range?

🕐 *Time to Code:*

**Index:**_____

**Code(s):** _____

## 2.

### Operative Report

PREOPERATIVE DIAGNOSIS: Dysfunctional uterine bleeding

POSTOPERATIVE DIAGNOSIS: Same

OPERATIONS: ThermaChoice balloon endometrial ablation

PROCEDURE: The patient was taken to the OR and, under adequate anesthesia, she was prepped and draped in the dorsolithotomy position for a vaginal procedure. The ThermaChoice system was assembled and primed. The catheter with the balloon was placed inside the endometrial cavity and slowly filled with fluid until it stabilized at a pressure of approximately 175–180 mm Hg. The system was then preheated to 87 degrees C. Eight minutes of therapeutic heat was applied to the lining of the endometrium. The fluid was allowed to drain from the balloon, and the system was removed. The procedure was discontinued.

✎ *Abstract from Documentation:*

What technique was used to destroy the lining of the uterus?

🕐 *Time to Code:*

**Index:**_____

**Code(s):** _____

## 3.

### Operative Report

PREOPERATIVE DIAGNOSIS: Desire for sterilization

POSTOPERATIVE DIAGNOSIS: Desire for sterilization

PROCEDURE: Postpartum tubal ligation

PROCEDURE IN DETAIL: The patient was taken to the operating room with an IV line in place. She was placed on the operating room table, and a 1.5-cm incision was made in the inferior fold of the umbilicus, continued through the subcutaneous tissue, rectus fascia, and parietal peritoneum as the incision was tracked ventrally using Allis clamps. Peritoneum was entered without difficulty. There was no evidence of vessel damage. Retractors were placed in the incision. At first, the left tube was visualized, grasped with a Babcock clamp, and pulled into the operative field. A hemostat was placed in an avascular plane of mesosalpinx, and a segment of tube was isolated and tied off using 2-0 plain gut. The segment was dissected and handed off the field. Pedicles were bovied. No active bleeding was noted. This was repeated on the opposite side.

Fascia and peritoneum were closed together using running continuous interlocking sutures of 0 Vicryl on a cutting needle. The wound was dressed, and the patient was taken to recovery in good condition.

### Abstract from Documentation:

Refer to the key term in the Alphabetic Index. What information is needed to assign a CPT code for this procedure?

### Time to Code:

**Index:** _____

**Code(s):** _____

## 4.

### Operative Report

PREOPERATIVE DIAGNOSIS: Perimenopausal bleeding; possible endometrial hypoplasia

POSTOPERATIVE DIAGNOSIS: Perimenopausal bleeding

PROCEDURES: Hysteroscopy; dilatation and curettage

SPECIMEN TO LAB: Endometrial curetting

ESTIMATED BLOOD LOSS: Less than 5 mL

DESCRIPTION OF PROCEDURE: The patient was taken to the operating room and under satisfactory general anesthesia was examined and noted to have a normal-size uterus. No adnexal masses noted. She was prepped and draped in the routine fashion, the speculum placed in the vagina, and the anterior lip of the cervix grasped with a single tooth tenaculum. The uterus sounded to 8 cm and easily admitted a #21 K-Pratt, so no further dilation was necessary. A 12-degree hysteroscope was placed, using lactated Ringer as the distending medium, and the cervical canal was normal. The cavity revealed just fronds of tissue. There was tissue sticking out that did not have a particularly polypoid appearance. No other lesions could be appreciated that were polypoid. Curettage with a Milan curette and a serrated curette and then polyp forceps being introduced revealed minimal tissue, and one piece of tissue of 5 mm that might be consistent with what was seen on previous sonogram. The hysteroscope was then replaced. No other lesions could be appreciated, and the walls appeared smooth. At this time, the hysteroscope and the tenaculum were removed. The tenaculum site was touched with silver nitrate. The bleeding was minimal at the end of the procedure. She was taken to the recovery room in satisfactory condition.

### Abstract from Documentation:

What procedures were performed?

Refer to the coding textbook. What guidelines pertain to this case?

### Time to Code:

**Index:** _____

**Code(s):** _____

## 5.

**Operative Report**

This 74-year-old woman underwent a partial vulvectomy 6 months ago for carcinoma in situ. She now was found to have recurrent disease of her vulva, and a partial vulvectomy was performed. The skin was dissected toward the introitus, and the posterior vagina was dissected for approximately 1 in. into the proximal vagina. The vaginal mucosa was undermined for at least 2 cm and approximated to the perineal skin by interrupted 2-0 Vicryl sutures. The anterior vulva lesion was then excised with a margin of approximately 0.5 cm. The lesion itself was approximately 2 cm in diameter. Bleeding points were cauterized. Wounds closed with interrupted 3-0 Vicryl.

Pathology Report: Specimens: vulva lesion with anal margin, anterior vulva, periurethral

*Abstract from Documentation:*

Review the Alphabetic Index for coding selections for vulvectomy procedures. What documentation is needed for the coding selection?

Note the definitions for simple, radical, partial, and complete vulvectomy codes (listed before code 56405). What documentation from this operative note leads you to the correct definition?

Was this a *radical* (removal of skin and deep subcutaneous tissue) or *simple* (removal of skin and superficial subcutaneous tissue) procedure?

*Time to Code:*

**Index:** _____

**Code(s):** _____

## 6.

**Operative Report**

The patient is a 59-year-old Gravida 3, Para 3, who was experiencing postmenopausal bleeding for the last five months, and her evaluation included a normal endometrial biopsy. The patient also was found to have a right adnexal mass on CAT scan confirmed with ultrasound, as well as a small cystic mass in the left ovary. Given the patient's age and despite a normal CA-125, the need for surgical evaluation of the complex adnexal mass was discussed. The patient also preferred a total abdominal hysterectomy to be performed because of postmenopausal bleeding and to see a definitive diagnosis and treatment of that condition. Informed consent was obtained for hysterectomy and bilateral salpingo-oophorectomy.

*Abstract from Documentation:*

Review the Alphabetic Index for the selection under the term Hysterectomy. What documentation is needed to locate a coding selection?

*Time to Code:*

**Index:** _____

**Code(s):** _____

# Nervous System Exercises

## Exercise 4.33: Medical Terminology Review Crossword Puzzle

Answers are located in Appendix A

**Across**

1. Space around dura mater in spinal cord
5. Vertebra of neck
6. Base of spine

**Down**

2. Surgical removal of vertebrae
3. Major nerve runs back of thigh
4. Tumor of nerves

## Exercise 4.34: Clinical Concepts

Fill in the blanks to the following scenarios. Choose from one of the two answers provided in parentheses.

1. Which of the following procedures would be performed to treat a patient diagnosed with Parkinson's disease? _____ (spinal fusion, insertion of neurostimulator)

2. As a result of a traumatic injury, the surgeon sutures the severed nerve. This procedure is known as a _____ (neurorrhaphy, neurolysis).

3. Surgical treatment of carpal tunnel syndrome would be documented as _____ (release compression of median nerve, neuroplasty of median nerve).

4. The patient is given 40 mg/mL IM of Depo-medro® for relief of pain. For coding purposes, this injection would be considered a _____ (single injection, continuous infusion).

## Exercise 4.35: Nervous System Coding Drill

Review the documentation and underline key term(s). Identify the terms used to look up the code selection in the Alphabetic Index. Assign CPT codes to the following cases. If applicable, assign CPT/HCPCS Level II modifiers.

1. Operative Note for Cervical Epidural Injection: Patient has been experiencing neck pain for several years. Using fluoroscopic guidance, an epidural needle is inserted into the epidural space. A combination of an anesthetic and cortisone steroid solution is injected into the epidural space.

   *Abstract from Documentation:*

   Refer to *Basic Current Procedural Terminology and HCPCS Coding* for guidance on coding for spinal injections. What documentation is needed for coding selection?

   Additional Resource: http://www.spine-health.com

   *Time to Code:*

   **Index:**_____

   **Code(s):** _____

2. The patient was diagnosed with an encephalocele at the base of the skull. For surgical intervention, a craniotomy for repair was performed.

   **Index:**_____

   **Code(s):** _____

3. The surgeon sutures a lacerated digital nerve of the left hand, a result of injury.

   **Index:**_____

   **Code(s):** _____

4. With the use of an operating microscope, the surgeon performed a repair of lacerated digital nerve of left index finger and left thumb.

   **Index:** _____

   **Code(s):** _____

5. Under imaging guidance, the patient undergoes an epidural injection of a neurolytic agent at the L5 joint.

   **Index:** _____

   **Code(s):** _____

6. Needle aspiration of cerebrospinal fluid for pseudocyst

   **Index:** _____

   **Code(s):** _____

7. Operative Note: Patient has lumbar stenosis at L3–4 and L4–5. Surgeon performed a right partial L3 and partial L4 hemilaminectomy with undermining laminotomy for decompression of nerve roots.

   **Index:** _____

   **Code(s):** _____

8. Cervical anterior discectomy with decompression of spinal cord, single interspace

   **Index:** _____

   **Code(s):** _____

9. Patient was diagnosed with a subdural hematoma. The surgeon created two left-sided burr holes for evacuation of the blood.

   **Index:** _____

   **Code(s):** _____

10. Surgeon removes a complete cerebrospinal fluid shunt system with no replacement.

    **Index:** _____

    **Code(s):** _____

## Exercise 4.36: Case Studies—Nervous System Operative Reports

Answers to exercises 1 and 2 are located in Appendix A, the remaining answers are only provided to educators.

### 1.

**Operative Report**

PREOPERATIVE DIAGNOSIS: Spinal cord stimulator battery replacement

POSTOPERATIVE DIAGNOSIS: Spinal cord stimulator battery replacement

OPERATION PERFORMED: Removal of spinal cord stimulator batteries and replacement with new batteries

No complications

No specimens

INDICATIONS FOR SURGERY: Patient is a 67-year-old man who had spinal cord stimulator implanted approximately five years ago. He comes back because of lack of functioning in this system. Decision was made to proceed with removal of the old batteries and replacement with new ones. The patient understands the risks and benefits of the procedure.

DESCRIPTION OF SURGERY: The patient was placed in supine position, and the area where the batteries were located on the left side was prepped and draped in the sterile fashion. The patient was infiltrated with lidocaine 1 percent. It was reopened with a #15 blade, and then the batteries were removed from the pocket and disconnected from the lead wires. A new battery system was reconnected. Wound was closed with #3-0 Vicryl and staples for skin.

✎ *Abstract from Documentation:*

What is a spinal cord stimulator?

🕐 *Time to Code:*

**Index:** _____

**Code(s):** _____

---

### 2.

#### Operative Report

PREOPERATIVE DIAGNOSIS: Radial digital nerve injury, right index finger

POSTOPERATIVE DIAGNOSIS: Radial digital nerve injury, right index finger

OPERATION PERFORMED: Primary repair of the radial digital nerve, right index finger

ANESTHESIA: General

ESTIMATED BLOOD LOSS: Minimal

TOURNIQUET TIME: 70 minutes

COMPLICATIONS: None

INDICATIONS FOR OPERATION: The 32-year-old male patient sustained a right index finger laceration while working. The patient lacerated the right index finger and was found to have altered sensibility along the radial aspect of the right index finger. The patient presented to the office and was diagnosed with a digital nerve laceration. Risks and benefits of the operation have been discussed with the patient. He now presents for operative exploration and repair.

DESCRIPTION OF PROCEDURE: After informed consent was obtained, the patient was given 1 gram of intravenous antibiotics. He was subsequently taken to the operating room and placed in the supine position with the right arm extended. Bilateral sequential compression boots were applied, and the patient was placed under general anesthesia without difficulty. The right upper extremity was prepped and draped in the usual sterile manner. The arm was then elevated, exsanguinated, and the axillary tourniquet was inflated to 250 mmHg.

The right index finger laceration was opened and was extended both proximally and distally in a zig-zag manner to facilitate wound exposure. The skin flaps were dissected with a #15 blade and were held in position with interrupted 4-0 nylon sutures. The subcutaneous tissues were gently dissected and the proximal and distal aspects of the radial digital nerve were identified. There was found to be a 100 percent transection of this nerve.

At this point, the operating room microscope was brought into the field, and the remaining portion of the operation was performed under the microscope. Proximal and distal nerve ends were identified and were released from all adjacent soft tissue structures. The proximal and distal ends were subsequently transected to create fresh edges for suturing. A primary end-to-end epineurial repair was then performed at the radial digital nerve utilizing interrupted 9-0 nylon sutures. At the end of the repair, the nerve was found to be in an excellent approximation. Two small pieces of Gelfoam were then placed around the nerve coaptation site.

The tourniquet was deflated. Bleeding points were controlled with direct pressure and hand elevation. The skin was then closed in one layer with interrupted 5-0 Prolene suture. Antibiotic ointment was then applied to the incision line.

Gauze dressing, cast padding, and a dorsally based plaster splint were then applied to the hand, maintaining the hand in a slightly flexed position. The patient tolerated the procedure very well and was withdrawn from general anesthesia without complications and transported to the recovery area in good condition. The patient will go home today with prescriptions for both antibiotics and pain medications. He will then follow up with us in the office next week for initial wound evaluation.

### Abstract from Documentation:

What is another medical term that describes repair?

### Time to Code:

**Index:** _____

**Code(s):** _____

## 3.

**Operative Report**

PREOPERATIVE DIAGNOSIS: Left ulnar nerve entrapment at the elbow

POSTOPERATIVE DIAGNOSIS: Left ulnar nerve entrapment at the elbow

PROCEDURE: Left ulnar nerve decompression at the elbow

INDICATIONS: The patient has a history of numbness in the fourth and fifth digits of the left hand and also some weakness in the grip. He complains of pain in the ulnar side of the left arm. He had an EMG, which was positive for entrapment of the left ulnar nerve at the elbow, and he had conservation treatment with some improvement of the mode of function, with severe significant numbness and pain. Because of the symptoms, the decision was made to proceed with a decompression of the left ulnar nerve at the elbow.

DESCRIPTION OF SURGERY: The patient was placed in supine position with the left hand on the surgical stand. The arm was then prepped, draped, and then an incision was marked at the level of the left elbow. The incision was infiltrated with lidocaine 1 percent and then the incision was made with a #15 blade. With the use of bipolar coagulator, the bleeding was easily controlled and then the ulnar nerve was exposed at the level of the elbow proximally and distally. The ulnar nerve was completely compressed and was released from a dense scar. Antibiotic solution was used to irrigate the area, and then the area was closed with #3-0 Vicryl and staples.

✎ *Abstract from Documentation:*

What procedure was performed (key operative term)?

What is the location of the nerve entrapment?

🕐 *Time to Code:*

**Index:**_____

**Code(s):**_____

## 4.

### Operative Report

PREOPERATIVE DIAGNOSIS: Right carpal tunnel syndrome

OPERATION: Right carpal tunnel release

INDICATIONS: The patient is a 55-year-old man who has a history of right hand pain and numbness. He was found to have a right carpal tunnel syndrome by EMG. The patient has been treated conservatively without any improvements, so a decision was made to proceed with a release of the right carpal tunnel.

DESCRIPTION: The patient was placed supine on the operating table, where the right hand was anesthetized with lidocaine 1 percent. An incision was made with a #15 blade down to the ligament, which was incised and was split with sharp scissors. The nerve was found to be completely free. The area was irrigated with antibiotic solution, and then the area was closed with #3-0 Vicryl and #4-0 nylon for the skin.

🕐 *Time to Code:*

**Index:**_____

**Code(s):**_____

## 5.

### Operative Report

PREOPERATIVE DIAGNOSIS: L5–S1 herniated disc on the left side

POSTOPERATIVE DIAGNOSIS: L5–S1 herniated disc on the left side

OPERATION: L5–S1 discectomy and L5 nerve root decompression

INDICATIONS FOR SURGERY: The patient is a 53-year-old male who has a history of low back pain and left leg pain in the L5 distribution. An MRI shows the presence of a herniated disc at L5–S1 migrated up impinging the L5 nerve root on the left side. The patient has been treated conservatively without any improvement.

DESCRIPTION OF SURGERY: The patient was intubated and placed in prone position. Then an incision was marked on the lower back and was prepped and draped in sterile fashion. The incision was made with a #10 scalpel, Bovie coagulator, and down to the fascia. At this point, the fascia was incised with a #15 blade. A flap of the fascia was then retracted with #2-0 Vicryl, and the muscle was gently dissected and retracted with a Taylor retractor. Under the microscope, a curette was placed between the L5 and S1, and x-rays were obtained. The x-rays showed that the curette was between L5 and S1 until under the microscope with microdissection, and with the use of a Midas Rex the lamina of L5 was partially drilled off and yellow ligament was opened, removed, and then the L5 nerve root was identified. A large herniated disc was then found, removed, and the L5 nerve root was completely decompressed. At this point, the interspace at L5 and S1 was entered for the disc removed laterally, and then a complete decompression of the L5 into the foramen was accomplished. At this point, the area was irrigated with antibiotic solution and a paste of Depo-Medrol, Amicar, and morphine was left in place. The fascia was closed with a #2-0 Vicryl, subcutaneous tissue with a #3-0 Vicryl, and the skin was closed with subcuticular #4-0 Vicryls.

### Abstract from Documentation:

Refer to *Basic Current Procedural Terminology and HCPCS Coding* for coding guidance. What is a discectomy?

After the location of the curette was confirmed, what was the first surgical action?

Refer to this term in the Alphabetic Index.

### Time to Code:

**Index:** _____

**Code(s):** _____

# Eye and Ocular Adnexa Exercises

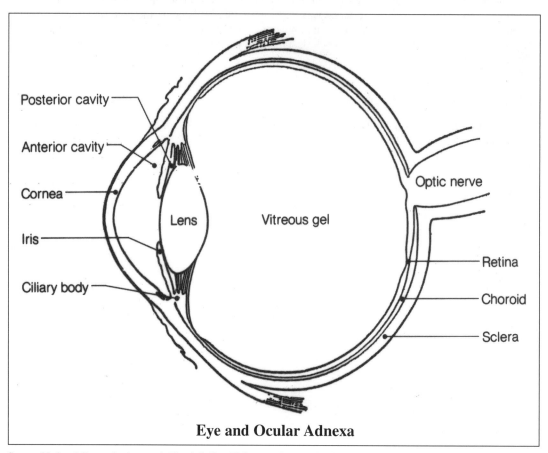

**Eye and Ocular Adnexa**

Source: National Cancer Institute. n.d. VisualsOnline. Unknown photographer/artist. http://visualsonline.cancer.gov/details .cfm?imageid=1767.

# Exercise 4.37: Medical Terminology Review Crossword Puzzle

Answers are located in Appendix A.

**Across**

2. Cyst of eyelid

3. Opening of tear duct

5. Drooping of eyelids

6. Eyes deviate outward

7. Benign growth of conjunctiva

**Down**

1. Inner part of eyelid

4. Abnormal alignment of eyes

## Exercise 4.38: Clinical Concepts

Fill in the blanks to the following scenarios. Choose from one of the two answers provided in parentheses.

1. A patient is diagnosed with crossed eyes. Which of the following procedures would be performed to correct this condition? _____ (vitrectomy, strabismus surgery)

2. Which of the following procedures is associated with treatment of glaucoma? _____ (lensectomy, trabeculectomy)

3. Which of the following procedures is associated with treatment of retinal detachment? _____ (scleral buckling, keratoplasty)

4. The patient presents with a small bump in the eyelid as a result of a clogged oil gland. The surgeon performs an excision for removal of the _____ (chalazion, blepharoptosis).

5. The patient is seeking treatment for extreme dry eyes. Which of the following procedures would be used to treat this condition? _____ (insertion of punctal plugs, phacoemulsification)

## Exercise 4.39: Eye and Ocular Adnexa Coding Drill

Review the documentation and underline key term(s). Identify the terms used to look up the code selection in the Alphabetic Index. Assign CPT codes to the following cases. If applicable, assign CPT/HCPCS Level II modifiers.

1. Patient diagnosed with exotropia. Surgeon performs bilateral recession of lateral rectus muscles.

*Abstract from Documentation:*

What is the definition of exotropia?

Refer to *Basic Current Procedural Terminology and HCPCS Coding* textbook: How is the lateral rectus muscle classified (vertical or horizontal)?

*Time to Code:*

**Index:**_____

**Code(s):** _____

2. Operative Note: Chalazion incision and drainage of the right eye

Procedure: The right eye was prepped and draped for the procedure. Chalazion forceps were used to grasp the upper eyelid. The surface of the chalazion was incised. The contents of the chalazion were curetted. Chalazion forceps were removed. Hemostasis was achieved. Maxitrol ointment was placed in the eye with an overlying eye pad. The patient was transferred to the recovery area in stable condition.

✎ *Abstract from Documentation:*

Refer to Chalazion in the Alphabetic Index. What documentation is needed to assign a correct CPT code?

🕐 *Time to Code:*

**Index:** _____

**Code(s):** _____

3. Incision and drainage of abscess of the upper right eyelid

**Index:** _____

**Code(s):** _____

4. The surgeon excises a 0.5 cm lesion of the conjunctiva.

**Index:** _____

**Code(s):** _____

5. Under general anesthesia, the surgeon probes the nasolacrimal ducts with irrigation, bilaterally.

**Index:** _____

**Code(s):** _____

## Exercise 4.40: Case Studies—Eye and Ocular Adnexa Operative and Emergency Department Reports

**1.**

### Operative Report

PREOPERATIVE DIAGNOSIS: Dermatochalasis of bilateral upper eyelids

POSTOPERATIVE DIAGNOSIS: Dermatochalasis of bilateral upper eyelids

OPERATION: Bilateral upper lid blepharoplasty

INDICATIONS: Patient is a 41-year-old female with a history of progressive upper eyelid hooding related to her redundant skin. The patient complains that this makes her eyelids feel heavy and interferes with her vision, particularly when she is tired. Patient was seen in the Outpatient Clinic and offered bilateral upper lid blepharoplasty.

DETAILS: Patient brought to the operating room and placed on the operating table in supine position. After adequate intravenous sedation had been obtained, the patient's upper eyelids were marked for incision and infiltrated with 5 cc of 0.5 percent lidocaine mixed with 1:300,000 epinephrine in each lid. The patient's face and head were prepped and draped in the standard operative fashion. The previously marked bilateral upper lids were incised through the skin and the orbicularis muscle using #15 surgical blade. The marked segment was excised sharply with #15 surgical blade with adequate tension on the operative field. The excision was carried down through the muscle, and the fat layer was easily visible. This procedure was repeated identically on the opposite lid. Next, the middle fat pad, which was readily identifiable, was gently teased out with a concave applicator and forceps and the pad was removed with the Bovie cautery. Next, the medial fat pad was also dissected out using gentle blunt dissection. The fat pad was retracted into the field and removed using the electrocautery. The procedure was repeated identically on the opposite lid. The operative field was then examined for hemostasis. The electrocautery was used to dry up any small bleeders. The wound was closed in a single layer using interrupted #6-0 Ethibond sutures. The wounds were dressed with Bacitracin and iced moist gauze, and the patient was transferred to the recovery room in stable condition.

✎ *Abstract from Documentation:*

Refer to the key operative term in the Alphabetic Index and note the code range.

What documentation is needed from the record to correctly assign a CPT code(s)?

🕐 *Time to Code:*

**Index:** _____

**Code(s):** _____

## 2.

### Operative Report

Pterygium removal with conjunctival graft, right eye

PROCEDURE DETAILS: Local anesthesia was achieved with a 50/50 mixture of 2 percent lidocaine and 0.75 percent bupivacaine with hyaluronidase. The eye was prepped and draped in the usual sterile fashion. The lashes were isolated on Steri-Strips and the lids separated with the wire speculum. The pterygium was marked with a marking pen and subconjunctival injection of 1 percent lidocaine with epinephrine was injected underneath the pterygium. The pterygium was then resected, and the body of the pterygium was resected with sharp dissection with Westcott scissors. The head of the pterygium was dissected off the cornea with Martinez corneal dissector. The cornea was then smoothed with an ototome burr. Hemostasis was achieved with bipolar cautery.

A conjunctival graft measuring 10 × 8 mm was harvested from the superior bulbar conjunctiva by marking the area, injecting it with subconjunctival 1 percent lidocaine with epinephrine. This was dissected with Westcott scissors and sutured in place with multiple interrupted 9-0 Dexon sutures. Subconjunctival Decadron and gentamicin injections were given. A bandage contact lens was placed on the eye. Maxitrol ointment was placed on the eye. A patch was placed on the eye. The patient tolerated the procedure well and was taken to the recovery room in good condition.

✎ *Abstract from Documentation:*

What is a pterygium?

What procedure was used to correct this condition?

🕐 *Time to Code:*

**Index:** _____

**Code(s):** _____

## 3.

**Operative Note**

**Emergency Department Record**

Patient brought to the ED from work with complaints of a foreign body in the right eye. He was wearing safety glasses but stated a piece of metal flew in the eye. He reports slight irritation but no blurred vision. PERLA: Fundi without edema. There was no foreign body on lid eversion. Slit lamp shows a foreign body approximately 2–3 o'clock on the edge of the cornea. It appears to be metallic. Iris is intact. There are no cells in the anterior chamber.

PROCEDURE: Two drops of Alcaine were used in the right eye. With use of slit lamp, foreign body was removed without difficulty.

IMPRESSION: Residual corneal abrasion

DISPOSITION: Foreign body removed from right eye

*Abstract from Documentation:*

Why did the patient seek treatment in the Emergency Department?

What procedure (and technique) was performed?

*Time to Code:*

**Index:** _____

**Code(s):** _____

## 4.

DIAGNOSIS: Nasolacrimal duct obstruction

PROCEDURE: Nasolacrimal duct probing and irrigation for left eye

PROCEDURE DETAILS: The patient was brought into the operating room. The operative eye was prepped and draped. A punctal dilator was used to dilate the superior and inferior puncta of the operative eye. A double-O Bowman probe was passed through one of the puncta and passed into the common canaliculus. The probe was passed into the nasolacrimal sac and down the bony canal of the nasolacrimal duct. The probe was passed into the nasal cavity beneath the inferior turbinate. The probe was removed. A lacrimal cannula attached to a 3-cc syringe filled with fluorescein solution was used to cannulate the nasolacrimal duct. An aspirating catheter was placed in the ipsilateral nasal cavity. Fluorescein was irrigated into the nasolacrimal duct. Fluorescein was aspirated from the nasal cavity following the irrigation. This demonstrated patency of the nasolacrimal drainage system. The lacrimal cannula and aspiration catheter were removed. The patient tolerated the procedure well and was transferred to the recovery room in stable condition.

*Abstract from Documentation:*

What documentation is needed to assign the correct CPT code?

*Time to Code:*

**Index:** _____

**Code(s):** _____

# Auditory System Exercises

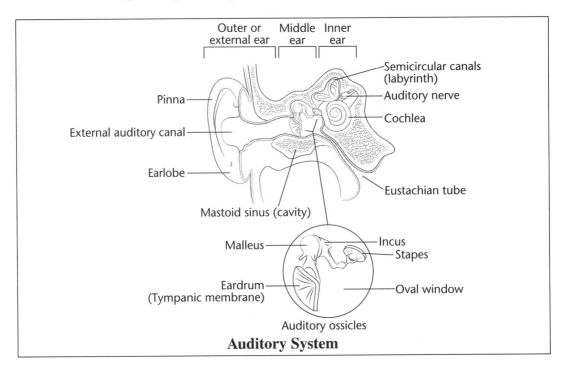

**Auditory System**

## Exercise 4.41: Medical Terminology Review

Match the following terms with the correct definition.

1. ____ myringotomy     A. connects middle ear with nasopharynx

2. ____ tympanoplasty     B. eardrum

3. ____ stapedectomy     C. surgical incision into eardrum

4. ____ Eustachian tube     D. surgical removal of innermost chain of three ossicles in middle ear

5. ____ tympanum     E. surgical repair of middle ear

## Exercise 4.42: Clinical Concepts

Fill in the blanks to the following scenarios. Choose from one of the two answers provided in parentheses.

1. The patient is seen for chronic middle ear infection. Conservative treatment with antibiotics would not clear the infection, so it was elected to perform a(n) _____ to remove the infection (mastoidectomy, otoplasty).

2. The patient was diagnosed with otosclerosis and as a result, cannot hear sound. The surgeon performs a _____, which removes a small bone and subsequently inserts a prosthesis to transmit sound (labyrinthectomy, stapedectomy).

3. Which of the following procedures is associated with reconstructive surgery of the eardrum? _____ (tympanoplasty, otoplasty)

## Exercise 4.43: Auditory System Coding Drill

Review the documentation and underline key term(s). Identify the terms used to look up the code selection in the Alphabetic Index. Assign CPT codes to the following cases. If applicable, assign CPT/HCPCS Level II modifiers.

1.  Physician Office Note

    Examination of the ear canal on both sides revealed impacted cerumen, tightly on the right side and a little bit on the left. With the use of ear curette, the impacted cerumen was removed. Both ears were irrigated with saline solution and suctioned dry to clean out all the debris.

    **Index:** _____

    **Code(s):** _____

2.  The surgeon performs a modified radical mastoidectomy for extensive spreading of cholesteatoma.

    **Index:** _____

    **Code(s):** _____

3.  The surgeon performs a bilateral otoplasty for the patient's protruding ears.

    **Index:** _____

    **Code(s):** _____

4.  The emergency department physician removes a pencil eraser from the external auditory canal of a 1-year-old patient.

    **Index:** _____

    **Code(s):** _____

## Exercise 4.44: Case Studies—Auditory Operative Reports

**1.**

### Operative Report

PREOPERATIVE DIAGNOSIS: Recurrent otitis media with persistent bilateral middle ear effusion

POSTOPERATIVE DIAGNOSIS: Same

PROCEDURE: Bilateral myringotomy with ventilating tube insertion

PROCEDURE IN DETAIL: The patient was prepped and draped in the usual fashion under general anesthesia. Myringotomy was performed in the anterior-inferior quadrant and thick fluid suctioned from the middle ear space. A Type I Paparella tube was then inserted. Then a myringotomy was performed on the left ear; again thick fluid was suctioned from the middle ear space. A Type I Paparella tube was then inserted. Cortisporin Otic Suspension drops were then placed in both ear canals and cotton in the ears. The patient was awakened and returned to the recovery room in satisfactory condition.

✏ *Abstract from Documentation:*

Refer to *Basic Current Procedural Terminology and HCPCS Coding* for guidelines pertaining to myringotomy for insertion of tubes. What coding guidance is provided in the textbook for this procedure?

🕐 *Time to Code:*

**Index:** _____

**Code(s):** _____

---

**2.**

### Operative Report

PREOPERATIVE DIAGNOSIS: Lesion of external auditory canal

POSTOPERATIVE DIAGNOSIS: Lesion of external auditory canal

OPERATION PERFORMED: Radical excision of external auditory canal lesion

INDICATIONS FOR PROCEDURE: This 34-year-old patient presents with a bleeding, friable, painful lesion of the ear canal. The lesion has apparently been present for eight months and has been unresponsive to topical therapy. An ulceration and raised areas suggest the possibility of basal cell.

DESCRIPTION OF OPERATION: Following the satisfactory instillation of oral endotracheal anesthesia, the right ear was prepped and draped in the usual fashion. Xylocaine and 1:100,000 epinephrine was instilled in the postaural area as well as endaural markings of the Lempert I and III incision, and the ear canal was injected with Xylocaine 1:50,000. The canal was debrided of ceruminous material, squamous debris, and copiously irrigated with Betadine and then sterile saline.

A modified Lempert endaural approach was now cut, and hemostasis was achieved with bipolar cautery. The lesion was identified, and a circumferential incision was made several millimeters lateral to the annulus with back-cuts being made along the tympanomastoid suture and then just cephalic to the upper portion of the lesion. The lesion does not extend to the cartilaginous junction, and a lateral incision was now made. Dissection was carried to the level of the periosteum, which was included as the lesion was now removed. A circumferential cuff of canal skin was now removed and sent for frozen section, which revealed no evidence of tumor. The postaural area was now prepared, and using a #11 blade, a split-thickness skin graft was harvested. The wound site was hemostased, and fresh Gelfoam with adrenaline was applied to the donor site.

The split-thickness skin graft was now contoured into the bony defect area and packed in place with Gelfoam. The cottonoid was applied to the ear canal. The postaural area was dressed. The patient was awakened from anesthesia. Permanent sections are pending on the mass. The patient was discharged to the recovery room in satisfactory condition.

✏ *Abstract from Documentation:*

Refer to Lesion, Auditory Canal, Excision, Radical in the Alphabetic Index.

What documentation is needed to differentiate between the code selections?

🕐 *Time to Code:*

**Index:** _____

**Code(s):** _____

# 3.

## Operative Report

PREOPERATIVE DIAGNOSIS: Conductive hearing loss, left ear

POSTOPERATIVE DIAGNOSIS: Conductive hearing loss, left ear

OPERATION: Stapedectomy

PROCEDURE: The patient was prepped and draped in the usual manner. The external auditory canal wall was injected with 1 percent lidocaine and 1:100,000 epinephrine. The tympanomeatal flap was elevated using a vertical rolling knife. The middle ear was entered and chorda tympani nerve identified and annulus lifted out of the tympanic sulcus. After elevating the tympanomeatal flap anteriorly, the ossicles were palpated, and the malleus and incus moved freely and the stapes was fixed. The posterior superior canal wall was curetted down after mobilizing the chorda tympani nerve, which was left intact. The stapes footplate was easily visualized and found to be markedly thickened. The pyramidal process was identified and the stapes tendon cut, and an IS joint knife was used to dislocate the joint between the incus and stapes. Next, a small and a large Buckingham mirror were used along with a drill to drill out the stapes footplate. After this was done, a 0.5 × 4-mm Schuknecht piston prosthesis was placed in position. Crimping was achieved, and there was an excellent fit, and the stapes footplate area was then packed with small pieces of Gelfoam. The tympanomeatal flap was then put back in proper position, and the middle ear was then packed with rayon strips of Cortisporin and a cotton ball in the middle to form a rosette. The patient was awakened in the operating room and transferred to recovery in no apparent distress.

## Abstract from Documentation:

What is a stapedectomy?

## Time to Code:

**Index:** _____

**Code(s):** _____

# 4.

## Operative Report

PREOPERATIVE DIAGNOSIS: Left tympanic membrane perforation

POSTOPERATIVE DIAGNOSIS: Left tympanic membrane perforation

PROCEDURE: Left tympanoplasty

INDICATIONS FOR OPERATION: This patient is a man who sustained a tympanic membrane perforation 20 years ago after diving into a pool. He has now sought repair.

DETAILS OF OPERATION: After induction of anesthesia, the table was rotated 180 degrees, and the left ear was prepped and draped in sterile fashion. Operating microscope was then used to inspect the left ear. A large central perforation encompassing approximately 50 percent of the tympanic membrane was visualized. Malleus was clearly visualized and appeared intact. Using 1 percent lidocaine with 1:1,000 epinephrine injection, four quadrant canal injection was performed. Next, the patient was rotated away and a postauricular incision was made. Temporalis fascia was harvested and kept aside. A T-shaped incision was made on soft tissue, and Lempert elevator was used to elevate the canal walls again. A freer was used to elevate the canal walls again and the previously made canal wall incisions were identified. The vascular flap was then raised. Canal wall skin was elevated to the level of the annulus, which was then elevated. The middle ear space was entered through the mucosa using a Rosen. The chorda tympani nerve was identified and preserved. The tympanic membrane was then raised off the chorda tympani nerve and the malleus. Gelfoam was placed in the anterior-most aspect of the middle ear space, and the fascia was then laid into place. Tympanic membrane was laid down over the fascia. The vascular flap was then laid back down and the postauricular incision was closed with Vicryl sutures. PSO ointment was applied to the middle ear space, and at this point, the left ear was cleaned. Sterile dressing was then placed over the ear and the patient was returned to the recovery room.

*Abstract from Documentation:*

Refer to Tympanoplasty in the Alphabetic Index.

What types of documentation should be searched for when reading the operative report?

*Time to Code:*

**Index:**_____

**Code(s):**_____

## Exercise 4.45: Multiple Choice Questions

Choose the correct coding assignment for the following surgical procedures.

1. The surgeon performed a nerve grafting procedure of the patient's hand, 2 cm in length.

    a. 64890
    b. 64891
    c. 64892
    d. 64895

2. The physician performed a complex wound repair of a 6.0 cm laceration of the arm.

    a. 13101
    b. 13120
    c. 13121
    d. 13132

3. The surgeon performs a direct laryngoscopy to remove a piece of hard candy.

    a. 31511
    b. 31530
    c. 31540
    d. 31577

4. The surgeon performed a nephrolithotomy for removal of a large staghorn calculus lodged in the renal pelvis and calyces.

    a. 50060
    b. 50065
    c. 50075
    d. 50130

5. Patient has advanced ovarian cancer and is now seen for removal of ascitic fluid in the abdomen. Under ultrasound guidance, the surgeon advanced the needle and aspirated the fluid.

   a. 49020
   b. 49062
   c. 49082
   d. 49083

6. The patient was diagnosed with neuritis of the medial calcaneal nerve. The physician performs a percutaneous alcohol nerve sclerosing (PANS) injection.

   a. 64620
   b. 64630
   c. 64632
   d. 64640

7. The surgeon performs an open reduction with internal fixation for a fractured femoral neck.

   a. 27230
   b. 27235
   c. 27236
   d. 27244

8. The patient presents with an area of calcification of the upper outer quadrant of the left breast identified on the mammogram. The surgeon excises the lesion and submits the specimen to pathology.

   a. 19120-LT
   b. 19125-LT
   c. 19301-LT
   d. 19303-LT

9. The patient has severe osteomyelitis of the fifth metatarsal head. The surgeon completely amputates the metatarsal head.

   a. 28104
   b. 28110
   c. 28111
   d. 28113

10. Imaging studies revealed that the patient has an esophageal stricture. The surgeon performs an EGD. Advanced through the endoscope, a balloon catheter is positioned and inflated to approximately 15 mm to dilate the stricture.

    a. 43245
    b. 43248
    c. 43249
    d. 43233

# Chapter 5

# Radiology

## Exercise 5.1: Medical Terminology Review

Match the following terms with the correct definition.

1. ____ CT scan
2. ____ Nuclear medicine
3. ____ MRI
4. ____ Ultrasound
5. ____ X-ray

A. Uses electromagnetic radiation to make images

B. Creates multiple images with computer technology to provide cross-sectional views

C. Uses powerful magnet and radio waves to take images

D. Uses high-frequency sound waves to view organs and structures in the body

E. Images developed based on energy emitted from radioactive substances

## Exercise 5.2: Case Studies

Identify the key term from the index and assign radiology codes to the following cases.

### Case Study #1

MRI Scan of the Pelvis

Clinical History: Reported fullness, status post hysterectomy and right side oophorectomy

Technique and Findings: Images through the pelvis were obtained utilizing axial, sagittal, and coronal projections. Pre- and post-contrast images were also obtained. Sagittal images show normal appearance of the fluid-filled bladder. There is a linear-type low signal structure interspersed between what appears to be the rectum and bladder. This appears to be a continuation of the vaginal cuff and perhaps represents scar tissue. This does not show any specific enhancement. I do not believe this represents any bowel. The remainder of the pelvis is otherwise unremarkable without findings of any free fluid or unusual adnexal masses. The osseous structures are unremarkable to include the iliac bones in both hips.

Impression: Linear shelf-like low attenuation signal interspersed between the fluid-filled cystic bladder and rectum. I am unclear to the exact significance of this finding. This may well represent a component of fibrosis or scar. This does not show any enhancement with contrast. I do not believe this represents any bowel loop. My recommendation for further evaluation would be CT scan of the pelvis with intravenous contrast to opacify the bladder and also rectal contrast to delineate the boundaries of the rectum. No clear indication of any contained mass or obvious free fluid.

**Index:** _____

**Code(s):** _____

## Case Study #2

X-Ray of Elbow, Three Views

Radiograph: Right elbow, three views

Indications: Pain in elbow after fall

Findings: There is a mildly displaced, slightly angulated fracture involving the supracondylar portion of the distal humerus. There is associated joint effusion reflecting hemarthrosis.

**Index:** _____

**Code(s):** _____

## Case Study #3

Oral Cholecystogram

The gallbladder concentrates the contrast medium well and numerous radiolucent calculi are demonstrated.

Diagnosis: Cholelithiasis

**Index:** _____

**Code(s):** _____

## Case Study #4

Upper Abdominal Ultrasound

The gallbladder, liver, pancreas, kidneys, and spleen are well delineated and appear normal. The bile ducts are not distended. The abdominal aorta and inferior vena cava are normal in caliber.

Opinion: Normal upper abdominal sonogram

**Index:** _____

**Code(s):** _____

## Case Study #5

KUB, Upper GI Series

The KUB study reveals a large amount of fecal matter present in the colon. Staples are seen in the right upper quadrant. The stomach is high and transverse in type. There is a small sliding hiatal hernia, and there is small gastroesophageal reflux. The duodenal bulb fills without ulceration. The stomach empties well.

Opinion: Small sliding hiatal hernia with intermittent gastrointestinal reflux

**Index:** _____

**Code(s):** _____

## Case Study #6

CT Scan of the Head

Technique: Noncontrast CT scan of the head

Findings: No evidence of acute bleed is noted. The ventricles are not dilated and are maintained in their midline position. No evidence of any low attenuation area, especially in the basal ganglia or in the brainstem, noted to suggest acute or old infarct. The posterior fossa appears normal. No abnormal calcifications are seen.

Impression: No evidence of acute bleed identified. No midline shift or acute infarct noted.

**Index:** _____

**Code(s):** _____

## Case Study #7

Bilateral Screening Mammogram

Comparison was made to multiple prior studies.

Findings: Examination demonstrates moderately dense fibroglandular tissue. A nodular density is seen in the left central areolar region, which was seen on the prior studies and is essentially unchanged. There is no evidence of any suspicious calcifications. Skin and nipples have no abnormality. As compared with prior study, there is no significant interval change.

Impression: No radiographic evidence of malignancy. No significant interval change since prior study.

**Index:** _____

**Code(s):** _____

## Case Study #8

CT Scan, Right Elbow

Tomographic cuts were taken through the elbow at 3 mm intervals in anteroposterior and lateral views. No bone or joint abnormalities are evident. No fracture is evident.

Impression: Normal right elbow

**Index:** _____

**Code(s):** _____

## Case Study #9

General Radiology

Chest, Posteroanterior (PA) and Lateral

Cardiomegaly is again noted. Left-sided pleural effusion is present. Increase interstitial lung markings are present bilaterally. No pneumothorax. Patchy airspace opacities in the mid-lungs bilaterally are present but slightly less prominent than on the previous portable chest-x-ray. Indistinctness of the hila is present. Bony structures are stable.

Impression: Cardiomegaly with indistinct hila and increased interstitial markings. This is favored to represent pulmonary edema. Recommend clinical correlation and follow plain films.

**Index:** _____

**Code(s):** _____

## Case Study #10

Left ankle (two views): The left ankle shows no evidence of fracture or dislocation. The visualized bones and their respective articular surfaces are intact.

Conclusion: Normal left ankle

**Index:** _____

**Code(s):** _____

## Case Study #11

KUB and Intravenous Pyelogram

The KUB is normal. No urinary calcifications can be identified.

Following the intravenous injection, there is a good delineation of the urinary tract. The kidneys are small, measuring 9.5 cm in their greatest length. The renal collecting system, ureters, and bladder appear normal.

Opinion: The kidneys measure slightly small. The urinary tract is otherwise normal.

**Index:** _____

**Code(s):** _____

## Exercise 5.3: Multiple Choice Questions

Answer the following multiple choice questions.

1. When coding CT scan of the abdomen, what documentation determines the code selection?

    a. number of views
    b. unilateral or bilateral
    c. use of contrast
    d. child or adult

2. The patient is seen in the Emergency Department for pain after falling down steps. The ED physician orders a CT scan of the thoracic spine. What is the correct code assignment?

    a. 72020
    b. 72070
    c. 72128
    d. 72129

3. A football player is injured and was transported to the hospital. An MRI of the shoulder (with contrast) was performed. What is the correct code assignment?

   a. 73020
   b. 73201
   c. 73221
   d. 73222

4. A 33-year-old pregnant female is 26 weeks gestation and considered large for dates. A transabdominal ultrasound is performed to determine the exact gestational age and to assess the fetus. What is the correct code assignment?

   a. a. 76801
   b. b. 76805
   c. c. 76811
   d. d. 76817

5. A female patient has a history of upper abdominal pain. Previous diagnostic studies were inconclusive. Her physician orders, from Nuclear Medicine, a hepatobiliary imaging study for suspected acute cholecystitis. What is the correct code assignment?

   a. 76700
   b. 78226
   c. 78227
   d. 78299

6. A patient has coronary artery disease and his physician wants to assess cardiac myocardial viability prior to coronary artery bypass surgery. This clinical history would justify which of the following diagnostic tests?

   a. 71010
   b. 71275
   c. 71550
   d. 75561

7. The diagnosis of acute diverticulitis would support medical necessity for which of the following?

   a. 72010
   b. 72220
   c. 72193
   d. 74300

8. Which of the following ultrasound procedures would be edited as an "error" if submitted on the claim for a male patient?

   a. 76830
   b. 76872
   c. 76881
   d. 76882

9. The patient is referred for a diagnostic ultrasound evaluation for a mass in the temporal retina. What is the correct code assignment?

   a. 76510
   b. 76529
   c. 76536
   d. 76770

10. A patient is suspected to have a sialolithiasis. Which of the following tests would be supported by this diagnosis?

    a. 70140
    b. 70170
    c. 70380
    d. 70490

# Chapter 6

# Pathology and Laboratory Services

## Exercise 6.1: Case Studies

Identify the key term from the index and assign pathology and laboratory codes to the following cases.

### Case Study #1

**GENERAL CHEMISTRY**

| Sodium | Potassium | Chloride | Total $CO_2$ | Glucose | BUN | Creatinine | Ionized Calcium |
|--------|-----------|----------|--------------|---------|-----|------------|-----------------|
| 138    | 3.3       | 96       | 34           | 104     | 20  | 0.8        | 6.0             |

Index: _____

Code(s): _____

### Case Study #2

A physician suspects that a patient might have an adrenocortical insufficiency and orders an insulin tolerance panel (cortisol and glucose) test.

Index: _____

Code(s): _____

### Case Study #3

An 8-year-old child presents in the urgent care center for abdominal pain associated with some diarrhea. The physician orders a fecal calprotectin test.

Index: _____

Code(s): _____

### Case Study #4

A 55-year-old female is seen in the physician's office for an elevated blood pressure. She reports that there is a family history of kidney disease. A Cystatin C blood test is performed.

Index: _____

Code(s): _____

## Case Study #5

**Pathology Report**

Specimen: Prostate chips from TURP

Gross Examination: One specimen is received in formalin labeled with demographics and prostate chips. It consists of gray-tan, rubbery fragments of tissue measuring in aggregate 2.9 × 2.5 × 1.5 cm. The specimen is entirely submitted in cassettes A1–A4.

Microscopic Examination: Benign prostatic hypertrophy

**Index:** _____

**Code(s):** _____

## Case Study #6

**Pathology Report**

Specimen: Nasal cyst

Gross Description: One specimen received in formalin labeled "nasal cyst." Skin measuring 1.7 × 0.8 × 0.5 cm. The specimen is serially sectioned revealing a 0.3 cm in diameter cyst containing white mucous-like material.

Microscopic Description: Skin, nose consistent with sebaceous adenoma

**Index:** _____

**Code(s):** _____

## Case Study #7

**Lipid Panel**

| Test | Result | Reference Ranges |
|------|--------|------------------|
| Cholesterol, serum | 206 | 75–200 |
| HDL | 51 | 30–70 |
| Triglycerides | 119 | 20–250 |

**Index:** _____

**Code(s):** _____

## Case Study #8

**Toxicology/Drug Levels**

| Procedure | Result | Units | Ref Range |
|-----------|--------|-------|-----------|
| Total Digoxin Level | 0.7 Low | ng/mL | 0.8–2.0 |

**Index:** _____

**Code(s):** _____

## Case Study #9

| Test Name | Glycohemoglobin |
|-----------|-----------------|
| Reference Range | 3.6–6.8 |
| Result | 5.9 |

**Index:** _____

**Code(s):** _____

## Case Study #10

A stool sample is submitted to the lab for *Helicobacter pylori*.

**Index:** _____

**Code(s):** _____

## Case Study #11

Urine Culture

Source: Straight catheter

Abundant Gram-positive cocci suggestive of Streptococci

>100,000 CFU/mL *Serratia marcescens*

>100,000 CFU/mL *Enterococcus* species

**Index:** _____

**Code(s):** _____

## Exercise 6.2: Multiple Choice Questions

1. Because of a family history of breast cancer, the patient undergoes full sequence genic testing for BRCA1 and BRCA2. What is the correct code assignment?

   a. 81216
   b. 81211
   c. 81214
   d. 81214, 81216

2. The patient undergoes screening for colon cancer that includes occult blood in stool with three guaiac test cards.

   a. 82270
   b. 82271
   c. 82272
   d. 82274

3. Which of the following tests would only be performed on an infant?

   a. 83872
   b. 83970
   c. 83993
   d. 84030

4. Which of the following tests would be performed if the physician suspected that the patient was diabetic?

    a.  82757
    b.  82941
    c.  82951
    d.  83010

5. What is the correct code for total hepatitis B core antibody (HBcAb) test?

    a.  86704
    b.  86706
    c.  86707
    d.  86708

6. Which of the following tests is commonly performed on females?

    a.  84436
    b.  84550
    c.  84588
    d.  84702

7. Which of the following tests for a type of fungal infection caused by breathing in spores often found in bird and bat droppings?

    a.  86378
    b.  86490
    c.  86510
    d.  86580

8. Which of the following tests would identify the patient's use of methohexital?

    a.  80324
    b.  80332
    c.  80345
    d.  80361

9. Which of the following CPT codes for panels would not pass the software sex edit check for a male patient?

    a.  80047
    b.  80051
    c.  80055
    d.  80076

10. Which of the following CPT codes would not pass the software age edit check for a 65-year-old female?

    a.  81025
    b.  82040
    c.  82140
    d.  82175

# Chapter 7

# Evaluation and Management Services

## Exercise 7.1: Case Studies

Answer the following questions and assign Evaluation and Management codes to the following cases.

### Case Study #1

The patient was seen in the physician's office after falling and injuring her ankle. The physician performed a brief HPI, Review of Systems, a problem-focused exam, and the decision making was straightforward. What component(s) of the history is missing from this scenario?

Answer: _____

### Case Study #2

A new patient is seen in the physician's office for dull ache in his left side. The physician performs a detailed history and physical examination, and the medical decision making was of moderate complexity. What is the correct E/M code for this service?

Answer: _____

### Case Study #3

A 92-year-old new patient is seen in the patient's home to evaluate symptoms that include a cough and fever. The patient has a history of diabetes, and the family does not wish the patient to be hospitalized. A comprehensive history and examination with high-complexity decision making is performed. What is the correct E/M code assignment for this service?

Answer: _____

### Case Study #4

A 55-year-old patient (post LASIK surgery) visits a new ophthalmologist for extreme dry eyes. The physician performs an expanded problem-focused history and exam and prescribes eye drops as needed. What is the correct E/M code assignment for this service?

Answer: _____

### Case Study #5

A patient is seen on January 23, 20XX, by a primary care physician who is a member of University Associates. A cardiologist (also a member of University Associates) sees the patient on November 24 of the following year. Would the visit on November 24 be classified as a *new* or *established* patient?

**Answer:** _____

### Case Study #6

A patient is seen in the Emergency Department for severe low back pain. The ED physician performs an expanded problem-focused history, problem-focused examination, and the medical decision making was of moderate complexity. What is the correct E/M code assignment for this service?

**Answer:** _____

### Case Study #7

The physician sees a patient in Sunny Acres Nursing Facility as a follow-up visit. The patient has a urinary tract infection that is not responding to medication. The physician documents a problem-focused interval history, expanded problem-focused exam, and the medical decision making was of moderate complexity. What is the correct CPT code assignment for this service?

**Answer:** _____

### Case Study #8

An established patient is seen in the physician's office for counseling after having an extremely high cholesterol reading and hypertension. Which range of codes would be used to select the appropriate CPT code for these services?

**Answer:** _____

### Case Study #9

Physician documents that critical care services were provided to a 12-year-old patient for 45 minutes. What is the correct E/M code assignment for this service?

**Answer:** _____

### Case Study #10

The physician documents that the patient has a cough, fever, and muscle aches. A review of systems is performed, a detailed account of present illness is documented, and the physician outlines the management options, complexity of treatment plan, and orders tests. What key E/M component is missing from this documentation?

**Answer:** _____

**Case Study #11**

A 49-year-old established patient visits his family physician for a physical that is required by his place of employment. The physician documents a comprehensive history, performs an exam, and orders a series of routine tests such as a chest x-ray and EKG. In addition, the physician counsels the patient about his smoking habit. What CPT code would be selected to represent this service?

Answer: _____

## Exercise 7.2: Multiple Choice Questions

1. A patient is admitted to Observation Care at a local hospital. On the initial visit, the physician performs a comprehensive history and exam and the medical decision making is of moderate complexity. What is the correct CPT code assignment for this service?

    a. 99218
    b. 99219
    c. 99220
    d. 99222

2. A patient is found unconscious and admitted to the critical care unit. The physician provides comprehensive services for two hours. What is the correct CPT code assignment for this service?

    a. 99291
    b. 99292 × 4
    c. 99291, 99292
    d. 99291, 99292 × 2

3. The physician visits a long-time resident of a nursing facility who has been experiencing a decline in mental status. During this subsequent visit, the physician performs a detailed interval history and detailed examination, and medical decision making was of high complexity. What is the correct CPT code assignment for this service?

    a. 99309
    b. 99310
    c. 99318
    d. 99326

4. What code(s) would be referenced when a physician performs an annual assessment for a nursing facility patient?

    a. 99307–99310
    b. 99315–99316
    c. 99318
    d. 99339–99340

5. The physician sees an inpatient for a follow-up visit after a knee replacement. The physician performs a problem-focused history and examination with medical decision making of moderate complexity. What is the CPT code assignment for this service?
   a. 99231
   b. 99232
   c. 99234
   d. 99235

6. Which of the following E/M Services requires all 3 key components met or exceeded?

   a. Established Patient Office Visit
   b. Subsequent Observation Care
   c. Subsequent Hospital Care
   d. Initial Nursing Facility Care

7. What documentation is necessary to assign an E/M code for comprehensive preventive medicine?

   a. Time physician spends with patient
   b. Time and age of patient
   c. New/Established patient and age of patient
   d. Time, age, and initial/subsequent

8. SOAP Progress Note

   Subjective: This child was brought in by her mother for drainage in both eyes for two days. Minimal cough, almost none. Runny nose and congestion, mild. There has been no vomiting or diarrhea. No ear pulling. There is no sore throat that mother is aware. The child has been acting normally. Eating and drinking normally. No skin rash that the mother noticed.

   Immunizations: Up to date

   Objective: The patient is alert and appropriate for age, in no acute distress. Cries on exam. Easily consoled. Flat anterior fontanelle. Conjunctivae are injected with bilateral exudates, excoriated from the drainage on the left eyelid. Both TMs were dull and red. Loss of landmarks in the left TM and is bulging. Rhinorrhea is present with purulent nasal drainage. Pharynx is negative. Neck is supple. No lymphadenopathy. Lungs are clear to auscultation. Abdominal exam is unremarkable. No rash. No petechiae. Child has normal color. Oximetry is 97 percent on room air. Vital signs were stable.

   Assessment:

   1. Bilateral otitis media

   2. Bilateral conjunctivitis—infectious

   Plan: Polytrim eye drops, 2 drops 4 times a day for 7 to 10 days. Gentle cleanse to reduce the excoriation and mattering. Zithromax 100 mg/5 mL, use as directed. Recheck the ears in 10 days, sooner if worse.

   What key documentation element is missing from this SOAP note?

   a. History of Present Illness
   b. Review of Systems
   c. Chief Complaint
   d. Social History

9. Reference the SOAP note above. What key element controls the selection for medical decision making?

   a. General appearance
   b. Age of patient
   c. Prescribed medications
   d. Follow-up treatment

10. A physician spends a total of 55 minutes with an established patient. Thirty-five minutes of this time were spent in counseling the patient due to the onset of a new disease. Twenty minutes of the visit were spent on examining the patient and deciding on treatment. The key component(s) in the selection of the E/M code is (are):

    a. History and examination
    b. Medical decision making
    c. Time
    d. Medical decision making and time

# Chapter 8
# Medicine

## Exercise 8.1: Case Studies

Identify the key term from the index and assign codes from the Medicine Section to the following cases.

### Case Study #1

A 55-year-old patient with Type II diabetes mellitus e-mails her registered dietitian to ask advice about adding a food product to her diet. The dietitian promptly responds to the question and keeps a record of this correspondence. The date of the last visit was two weeks ago.

    **Index:**_____

    **Code(s):** _____

### Case Study #2

A 59-year-old female is undergoing treatment for metastatic colorectal cancer. Catheter was previously placed; she is now seen in the clinic with an attached implanted pump that needs to be refilled.

    **Index:**_____

    **Code(s):** _____

### Case Study #3

A 25-year-old patient receives an IM injection of meningococcal serogroup B vaccine (MenB), 3-dose schedule.

    **Index:**_____

    **Code(s):** _____

## Case Study #4

A 45-year-old patient with end-stage renal disease (ESRD) is seen in the outpatient dialysis clinic for services on July 2, 5, 9, 15, 18, 21, 24, and 28.

**Index:** _____

**Code(s):** _____

## Case Study #5

A 45-year-old patient complains of sneezing, coughing, and occasional episodes of wheezing. The physician wants to determine the cause of these allergic symptoms and performs 30 percutaneous skin tests.

**Index:** _____

**Code(s):** _____

## Case Study #6

Arterial Study
A 52-year-old female has a history of hypertension and now, during an examination, the physician hears carotid bruit. The physician orders a complete bilateral extracranial duplex ultrasound examination.

**Index:** _____

**Code(s):** _____

## Case Study #7

Photodynamic Therapy
Patient was diagnosed with actinic keratosis with lesions on several locations of the face. The physician prepares a topical solution and applies photosensitizing agent in topical solution form to each lesion.

**Index:** _____

**Code(s):** _____

## Case Study #8

Acute SLP Evaluation
Patient referred for a swallow evaluation. She was admitted for COPD exacerbation. She has a history of severe COPD and GERD. Chest CT showed concern for aspiration.
Oral and pharyngeal swallowing exam performed. Recommendation: no overt aspiration, given sips of liquid, bites of applesauce, and cracker. Voice remains clear, hyolaryngeal elevation/excursion feels adequate. Cannot rule out silent aspiration at bedside. Recommend modified barium swallow study.

**Index:** _____

**Code(s):** _____

## Case Study #9

A patient is seen in the Emergency Department with severe vomiting and diarrhea due to viral gastroenteritis. IV hydration prescribed and takes 1 hour to administer.

**Index:** _____

**Code(s):** _____

## Case Study #10

Electroencephalogram
Complaint: Altered mental status
Current Medications: Vasotec, Lanoxin, and Lasix
State of patient during recording: Awake and drowsy
Description: The background is characterized by diffuse slowing and disorganization consisting of medium-voltage theta rhythm at 4–6 Hz seen from all head areas. From anterior head areas, faster activity at beta range. Eye movements and muscle artifacts are noted. Photic stimulation and hyperventilation were not performed. Total recording time was 40 minutes.
Impression: This is a moderately abnormal record due to diffuse slowing and disorganization of the background, with the slowing being at theta range.

**Index:** _____

**Code(s):** _____

## Case Study #11

A 67-year-old patient with multiple medical problems is currently taking six prescriptions and several over-the-counter agents. The primary care physician has a concern about side effects; therefore, the patient is referred to a pharmacist for assessment and management of medications. The pharmacist assesses the treatment and makes recommendations during the 10-minute face-to-face visit.

**Index:** _____

**Code(s):** _____

## Exercise 8.2: Multiple Choice Questions

1. A 14-year-old patient has been diagnosed with seizures. Recently, the symptoms are worse; therefore, the physician orders a 24-hour digital 16 channel EEG with video. What is the correct code assignment?

   a. 95950
   b. 95953
   c. 95955
   d. 95956

2. A teenager has become defiant, refuses to go to school, and smokes marijuana. The parents disagree about how to handle the situation. A psychiatrist conducts a face-to-face interaction with the mother and father of the teenager. What is the correct code assignment?

   a. 90839
   b. 90845
   c. 90846
   d. 90847

3. The 28-year-old patient receives the first of three hepatitis B vaccination injections (IM). What is the correct code assignment?

   a. 90739
   b. 90471, 90739
   c. 90746
   d. 90471, 90746

4. A newly diagnosed patient with asthma is evaluated at the physician's office for use of a nebulizer. What is the correct code assignment?

   a. 94640
   b. 94642
   c. 94660
   d. 94664

5. A patient is seen for numbness and weakness in her right hand. The physician orders nerve conduction testing using preconfigured arrays for the right arm.

   a. a. 95905
   b. b. 95907
   c. c. 95885
   d. d. 95887

6. Six patients participated in a 45-minute group psychotherapy session. What is the correct code assignment?

   a. a. 90832
   b. b. 90834
   c. c. 90849
   d. d. 90853

7. What is the correct code assignment for a balloon angioplasty (PTCA) of right coronary artery with insertion of a drug-eluting stent?

   a. 92920-RC
   b. 92924-RC
   c. 92928-RC
   d. 92933-RC

8. What is the correct code assignment for a venous Doppler performed on both legs?

    a. 93925
    b. 93930-50
    c. 93962-50
    d. 93965

9. What is the correct code assignment for chemotherapy intra-arterial infusion, 50 minutes?

    a. 96401
    b. 96413
    c. 96420
    d. 96422

10. What is the correct code assignment for initial acupuncture treatment that required 4 needles and 15 minutes of personal contact with the patient?

    a. 97810
    b. 97811
    c. 97813
    d. 97814

# Chapter 9

# Anesthesia

## Exercise 9.1: Case Studies

Identify the key term from the index and assign anesthesia codes to the following cases.

### Case Study #1

This is a 49-year-old man with a chronic right-sided submandibular swelling occurring over the last few years. The diagnosis of right sialoadenitis was made. An excision of right submandibular gland was performed.

    **Index:** _____

    **Code(s):** _____

### Case Study #2

Through an abdominal approach, the surgeon performed a radical orchiectomy for a patient with cancer.

    **Index:** _____

    **Code(s):** _____

### Case Study #3

Patient admitted for uterine fibroids and dysmenorrhea. The surgeon performs a vaginal hysterectomy.

    **Index:** _____

    **Code(s):** _____

### Case Study #4

Patient is being treated for a lateral meniscus tear. The surgeon performs an arthroscopy meniscectomy.

    **Index:** _____

    **Code(s):** _____

## Case Study #5

The patient is a 65-year-old male who was recently treated for low anterior resection for a stage II superior rectal cancer. Adjuvant chemotherapy is planned. Placement of long-term venous access device was requested. Surgeon inserts a Port-a-Cath.

**Index:** _____

**Code(s):** _____

## Case Study #6

The patient has severe degenerative joint disease of the hip. The surgeon performs an open total hip arthroplasty using metal on poly.

**Index:** _____

**Code(s):** _____

## Case Study #7

Patient has a diagnosis of urinary retention. The surgeon performs a transurethral resection of the prostate.

**Index:** _____

**Code(s):** _____

## Case Study #8

The patient is a 56-year-old man previously diagnosed with pancreatic cancer. The surgeon performs a partial excision of the pancreas.

**Index:** _____

**Code(s):** _____

## Case Study #9

The patient is a 56-year-old male who presented to the ENT clinic with a history of left-sided nasal obstruction. The following procedures were performed: left maxillary sinusotomy, left anterior ethmoidectomy, and removal of left nasal polyposis.

**Index:** _____

**Code(s):** _____

## Case Study #10

The patient is a 76-year-old male with substantial underlying pulmonary disease. He has required mechanical ventilation for approximately two to three weeks and failed several attempts to be completely taken off mechanical ventilation. He was brought to the operating room for placement of a tracheostomy tube.

**Index:** _____

**Code(s):** _____

## Exercise 9.2: Multiple Choice Questions

Identify the correct Anesthesia code assignment for each of the following surgical procedures.

1.  Arthroscopic repair of tendon, elbow to shoulder

    a. 01710
    b. 01712
    c. 01714
    d. 01732

2.  Open reduction and internal fixation for fractured shaft of tibia

    a. 01462
    b. 01470
    c. 01480
    d. 01490

3.  Rhinoplasty to correct a deviated septum

    a. 00160
    b. 00162
    c. 00164
    d. 00190

4.  Inguinal hernia repair with mesh for a 44-year-old patient

    a. 00830
    b. 00834
    c. 00836
    d. 00840

5.  Closed manipulation of non-displaced fracture of the humerus

    a. 01710
    b. 01730
    c. 01740
    d. 01770

6.  Anterior cervical discectomy and fusion

    a. 00600
    b. 00604
    c. 00620
    d. 00670

7.  Patient treated in the interventional radiology suite for a percutaneous thrombectomy of the femoral vein

    a. 01916
    b. 01922
    c. 01924
    d. 01930

8. Craniotomy for excision of glioma

   a. 00190
   b. 00210
   c. 00211
   d. 00218

9. Direct coronary artery bypass grafting without pump oxygenator

   a. 00560
   b. 00561
   c. 00566
   d. 00567

10. Diagnostic studies revealed that the patient had an abdominal aortic aneurysm. In the interventional radiology suite, the patient had a placement of an abdominal aortic stent graft through a femoral artery approach under fluoroscopic guidance.

    a. 01916
    b. 01922
    c. 01926
    d. 01930

# Chapter 10

# HCPCS Level II

## Exercise 10.1: Case Studies

Identify the key term from the index and assign codes from the *HCPCS Level II* to the following cases.

### Case Study #1

Foam dressing to cover a wound. Sterile pad, 20 sq. in. without an adhesive border

    **Index:** _____

    **Code(s):** _____

### Case Study #2

Patient with asthma requires a nebulizer with compressor.

    **Index:** _____

    **Code(s):** _____

### Case Study #3

Patient has extreme dry eyes. Physician inserts temporary, absorbable lacrimal duct implants in each eye.

    **Index:** _____

    **Code(s):** _____

### Case Study #4

Patient is given oral prednisone, 5 mg.

    **Index:** _____

    **Code(s):** _____

## Case Study #5

Floating kyphosis pad

**Index:** _____

**Code(s):** _____

## Case Study #6

Standard metal bed pan

**Index:** _____

**Code(s):** _____

## Case Study #7

Portable paraffin bath unit

**Index:** _____

**Code(s):** _____

## Case Study #8

Handgrip for a cane

**Index:** _____

**Code(s):** _____

## Case Study #9

IV pole for infusion

**Index:** _____

**Code(s):** _____

## Case Study #10

Ocular implant

**Index:** _____

**Code(s):** _____

## Case Study #11

EMG biofeedback device

**Index:** _____

**Code(s):** _____

## Case Study #12

Clubfoot wedge to modify a shoe

**Index:** _____

**Code(s):** _____

## Case Study #13

Home blood glucose monitor

**Index:** _____

**Code(s):** _____

## Case Study #14

Injection 500 mg vancomycin HCL

**Index:** _____

**Code(s):** _____

## Case Study #15

Ostomy belt

**Index:** _____

**Code(s):** _____

## Case Study #16

Non-emergency transportation by wheelchair van

**Index:** _____

**Code(s):** _____

## Case Study #17

PAP smear (2 smears) performed by technician under the supervision of a physician

**Index:** _____

**Code(s):** _____

## Case Study #18

Injection, 10 mg protamine sulfate

**Index:** _____

**Code(s):** _____

## Case Study #19

Voice amplifier

**Index:** _____

**Code(s):** _____

**Case Study #20**

Hemodialysis machine

     **Index:** _____

     **Code(s):** _____

## Exercise 10.2: Multiple Choice Coding

1. Which of the following would be classified with a HCPCS Level II code?

    a. Medical Nutrition Therapy
    b. Legg Perthes orthosis
    c. McBride bunionectomy
    d. Salivary gland imaging

2. What is the correct HCPCS Level II code for a synthetic sheepskin pad?

    a. E0185
    b. E0188
    c. E0189
    d. E0196

3. What is the correct HCPCS Level II code for an injection of 250 mg of Ceftriaxone sodium?

    a. J0690
    b. J0692
    c. J0694
    d. J0696

4. What is the correct HCPCS Level II Medicaid code for a per diem residential habilitation waiver?

    a. T2014
    b. T2015
    c. T2016
    d. T2017

5. What is the correct HCPCS Level II modifier for services delivered under an outpatient physical therapy plan of care?

    a. GN
    b. GO
    c. GP
    d. GW

6. What is the HCPCS Level II code for bilateral, direct digital screening mammography?

    a. G0202
    b. G0204
    c. G0206
    d. 77056

7. What is the HCPCS Level II modifier for lower extremity prosthesis functional level 3?

   a. K0
   b. K1
   c. K2
   d. K3

8. Which of the following HCPCS Level II codes are designated for durable medical equipment?

   a. D codes
   b. E codes
   c. G codes
   d. H codes

9. Which of the following HCPCS Level II modifiers identifies the little finger of the right hand?

   a. F1
   b. F4
   c. F8
   d. F9

10. Which HCPCS Level II codes are designated for ambulance services?

   a. A codes
   b. B codes
   c. C codes
   d. D codes

# Chapter 11

# Reimbursement in the Ambulatory Setting

## Exercise 11.1: Crossword Puzzle

Answers are located in Appendix A.

### Across

2. Incorrectly assigning multiple codes
4. Develops yearly workplan
5. Assigning a code for higher payment
7. RVUs include physician work, practice, and _____ expenses
8. Reimbursement system for ambulatory surgery centers
9. Reimbursement system for physicians

### Down

1. Status indicator X identifies _____ services
3. Status indicator C describes _____ procedures
6. Tool used to weed out incorrect claims

## Exercise 11.2:

Review the following scenarios and answer the questions that follow.

### Exercise #1—Medical Necessity

A 47-year-old female patient is seen in an outpatient setting for a variety of symptoms, including fatigue, weakness, and insomnia. The physician orders the following tests:

```
FBS
PSA
WBC
T3, T4
TSH
```

Which test(s) does not meet medical necessity?

**Answer:** _____

### Exercise #2—Medical Necessity

Match the following diagnoses/symptoms with the appropriate test/procedure.

1. ____ R/O pregnancy          A. spirometry
2. ____ low back pain          B. EKG
3. ____ hearing loss           C. human chorionic gonadotropin (hCG)
4. ____ asthma                 D. osteopathic manipulative treatment
5. ____ coughing, sneezing, runny nose   E. tympanometry
6. ____ tachycardia            F. allergy tests

### Exercise #3—Medical Necessity

Which of the following diagnoses would support CPT code 51726 Complex cystometrogram?

a. menorrhagia
b. urinary tract infection
c. stress incontinence
d. dysurea

### Exercise #4—Medical Necessity

Which of the following codes would not be appropriate for a patient with the diagnosis of urethral stricture?

a. 52281
b. 52283
c. 52285
d. 52344

## Exercise #5—Medical Necessity

Which of the following diagnoses would be linked appropriately to CPT code 11640, Excision malignant lesion?

a. seborrheic keratosis of the cheek
b. melanoma of the forehead
c. melanocanthoma of the nose
d. nevus of the chin

## Exercise #6—Editing Codes

Which of the following sets of codes have age-specific descriptions in CPT?

a. Plastic repair of cleft lip
b. Diagnostic EGD
c. Repair of initial inguinal hernia
d. Cystourethroscopy

## Exercise #7—Editing Codes

Which of the following codes would not be appropriate for a female patient?

a. 19300  Mastectomy for gynecomastia
b. 25915  Krukenberg procedure
c. 27687  Gastrocnemius recession
d. 51705  Change of cystostomy tube; simple

## Exercise #8—Use of Modifiers

Place a check mark in front of each of the following CPT code(s) that should not be appended with a LT (left) or RT (right) HCPCS Level II modifier.

1. _____ 27816  Closed treatment of trimalleolar ankle fracture; without manipulation

2. _____ 28150 Phalangectomy, toe, each toe

3. _____ 11400 Excision, benign lesion including margins, except skin tag (unless listed elsewhere), trunk, arms, or legs; excised diameter 0.5 cm or less

4. _____ 19000 Puncture aspiration of cyst of breast

5. _____ 71060 Bronchography, bilateral, radiological supervision, and interpretation

6. _____ 58770 Salpingostomy

# Appendix A: Odd-numbered Answer Key

*Note that the answers distinguish the code from the modifier with a dash (-). For inputting codes electronically, the dash is not part of the code submission.*

## Chapter 1

# Introduction to Clinical Coding

### Exercise 1.1 CPT Code Selection

1. a

3. d

5. d

7. a

9. d

### Exercise 1.2 CPT Code Selections and Supportive Documentation

1. A surgeon performs a cystourethroscopy with dilation of a urethral stricture.

   CPT Code: 52341

   Correct Code: 52281

   **The documentation states that it was a <u>urethral</u> stricture. Correct code: 52281**

3. The surgeon repairs a ruptured abdominal aortic aneurysm.

   CPT Code: 35092

   Correct Code: 35082

   **There is no documentation of involvement of visceral vessels.**

5. The chiropractor documents that he performed osteopathic manipulation on the neck and back (lumbar/thoracic).

   CPT Code: 98925

   Correct Code: 98926

   **Note in the paragraph before code 98925, the body regions are identified. The neck would be the cervical region; the thoracic and lumbar regions are identified separately. Therefore, three body regions are identified.**

7. A 45-year-old patient has a repair of an initial incarcerated inguinal hernia.

   CPT Code: 49521

   Correct Code: 49507

   **The documentation supports the selection of the code for "initial" not "recurrent."**

9. The surgeon performs an excision of a 1.5 cm deep intramuscular soft tissue tumor of the scalp.

   CPT Code: 21011

   Correct Code: 21013

   **CPT distinguishes between an "intramuscular" soft tissue tumor excision from subcutaneous. Code 21011 is for a subcutaneous tumor, which does not match the documentation.**

## Exercise 1.3: Abstracting Documentation

**1.**

**Operative Note:**

PROCEDURE PERFORMED: Amniocentesis

REASON FOR PROCEDURE: The patient is a 30-year-old white female who is gravida 7, para 1, with intrauterine pregnancy at 36-4/7 weeks gestation. She was admitted in prodromal labor. She has gestational diabetes mellitus and an ultrasound suggesting fetal weight of greater than 10 pounds. The patient has been quite uncomfortable in recent weeks and is adamant about wanting to be delivered. In view of the gestational diabetes requiring insulin, I feel it important to document fetal lung maturity in a more or less elective delivery.

I discussed amniocentesis and the risks, benefits, and alternatives. After I answered her questions, she agreed to proceed with the procedure.

Description of the Procedure: Under ultrasound guidance a 4 to 5 cm pocket of amniotic fluid was identified in the fundal left side. The abdomen was prepped and draped. Under ultrasound guidance a 22-gauge needle was inserted into this pocket and approximately 8 cc of fluid was obtained, which was lightly bloodstained. I attempted to aspirate more using a second syringe but was unable to get further fluid so the procedure was terminated.

Assessment and Plan: Post procedure the fetal heart tracing was obtained and fetal heartbeat was in the 150s. Biophysical profile post procedure was 10 out of 10. We will await the amniocentesis results and if the l/s (lecithin/sphingomyelin) is mature, we will proceed with cesarean section.

✎ *Abstract from Documentation:*

Refer to Amniocentesis in the Alphabetic Index. What documentation is needed to select the applicable code range? Underline the portion of the operative report that supports your answer.

Answer: The documentation needs to support the reason for the procedure: diagnostic, therapeutic, or for an abortion.

CPT Code Assignment:

59000 Amniocentesis; diagnostic

## 3.

**Operative Report**

PREOPERATIVE DIAGNOSIS: Left upper lid laceration

POSTOPERATIVE DIAGNOSIS: Left upper lid laceration

PROCEDURE: Left upper lid laceration repair with exam under anesthesia

ANESTHESIA: General

COMPLICATIONS: There were no complications.

INDICATIONS: This 4-year-old child suffered a dog bite to his left upper lid and was unable to be repaired successfully in the emergency room. After obtaining informed consent, he was taken to the operating room.

DESCRIPTION OF THE PROCEDURE: The patient was prepped and draped in the usual sterile fashion. The wound margins were reapproximated using 6-0 absorbable suture and 2 lid margin sutures were placed using 6-0 silk. The injury was limited to the epidermis and part of the dermis. There was no structural damage to the blood vessels or deeper tissue layers. The lid was noted to be in good position, and then all skin lacerations were closed using a combination of 6-0 running and 6-0 interrupted nylon.

The patient then had his eye dilated, and exam under anesthesia was carried out using an indirect ophthalmoscope. There was no evidence of trauma to the globe or the posterior pole.

The patient was taken to the recovery room in good condition and will be sent home today to follow up in my office.

✎ *Abstract from Documentation:*

Refer to Repair, Eyelid in the Alphabetic Index. What code range is applicable?

Answer: Wound, Suture (67930–67935) The code selection is determined by extent of the wound repair; was it partial thickness or full thickness? Since the suturing was limited to the epidermis and part of the dermis, it is a partial thickness wound repair.

CPT Code Assignment:

67930-E1 Suture of recent wound, eyelid, involving lid margin, tarsus, and/or palpebral conjunctiva direct closure; partial thickness

## 5.

**Operative Report**

PROCEDURE: Upper endoscopy

INDICATION: The patient is a 45-year-old female who presents with five years of reflux symptoms. She has had some intermittent epigastric abdominal discomfort as well.

DESCRIPTION OF PROCEDURE: After obtaining informed consent and establishment of an intravenous line, the patient was positioned in the left lateral decubitus position. We used 10 mg of midazolam, 50 mcg of fentanyl, and supplemental oxygen at 2 liters per nasal cannula. She was monitored with pulse oximetry, continuous ECG tracing, and periodic blood pressure checks. A flexible video Olympus upper endoscope was passed through the oropharynx into the esophagus. The esophagus was unremarkable including the squamocolumnar junction at 36 cm from the incisors. Proximal gastric view including retroflexion showed minimal gastric valve laxity but was otherwise unremarkable. She had a series of three polyps in the general range of 5 to 7 mm in the mid gastric lumen, in line with the greater curvature of the stomach. One was more inflamed than the other two. All three were removed with standard snare polypectomy technique. The rest of the stomach was intact as was the pylorus, duodenal bulb, and second portion of the duodenum. All areas were resurveyed two additional times and we simply identified no additional findings. She tolerated the procedure well and without apparent complication.

Assessment: Gastric polyps as mentioned above. Otherwise unremarkable upper endoscopy.

### Abstract from Documentation:

What is an upper endoscopy?

Answer: An upper gastrointestinal endoscopy is a procedure that uses a lighted instrument (scope) to visualize the esophagus, stomach, and duodenum. The CPT code description also includes the possibility of visualizing the jejunum; however, this is not typical.

Did the physician just visualize the structures or perform another procedure during the endoscopy?

Answer: There were 3 polyps removed from the stomach, using a snare technique.

CPT Index Term (there may be several entries in the index leading to the correct range)

43247, 43250–43251 Endoscopy, Gastrointestinal, Upper, Removal

CPT Code Assignment:

43251 Upper gastrointestinal endoscopy including esophagus, stomach, and either the duodenum and/or jejunum as appropriate; with removal of tumor(s), polyps(s), or other lesion(s), by snare technique

## 7.

**Office Note**

HISTORY: The patient complains of bilateral ear pain. She denies any decrease in hearing. She has marked <u>cerumen impactions</u> in both ear canals. It took extensive <u>flushing</u> before I was able to get out the wax on both sides. Both canals are now patent.

PHYSICAL EXAMINATION: Vital signs are stable and she is afebrile.

ASSESSMENT: Bilateral cerumen impactions

PLAN: I told her she should irrigate both ears once a week with peroxide and warm water.

*Abstract from Documentation:*

What Alphabetic Index term can easily lead to the coding of this case?

Answer: Under the key term Cerumen, Removal the choices are with Instrumentation or with Irrigation/Lavage.

Underline the supportive documentation. Other than the fact that the physician flushed (irrigation) the ear canals to remove the wax, no other documentation is necessary besides unilateral and bilateral

CPT Code Assignment:

69209-50 Removal impacted cerumen (separate procedure), unilateral

A note appears under code 69210 that instructs to use modifier 50 if it is a bilateral procedure.

## Exercise 1.4: Crossword Puzzle

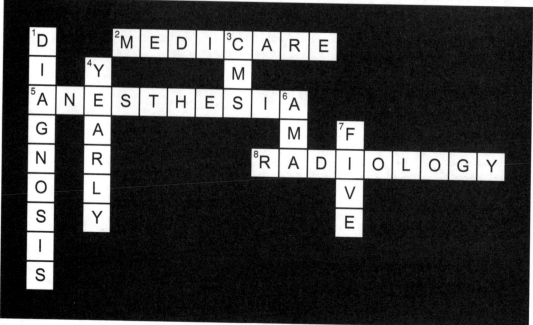

**Across**

2. Federal insurance for those over age 65 [MEDICARE]

5. Modifier P4 found in this CPT section [ANESTHESIA]

8. CT scans found in this section of CPT [RADIOLOGY]

**Down**

1. Supports medical necessity [DIAGNOSIS]

3. Agency administers Medicare [CMS]

4. A new edition of CPT is published _____ [YEARLY]

6. Organization that publishes CPT [AMA]

7. Number of digits in CPT code [FIVE]

# Chapter 2

# Application of the CPT System

## Exercise 2.1: Format and Organization of CPT

1. ____ Complete list of modifiers (**D**)

3. ____ 0210T Speech audiometry threshold, automated (**E**)

5. ____ 0503F Postpartum care visit (**B**)

## Exercise 2.2 Referencing *CPT Assistant*

Reference *CPT Assistant* to answer the following questions. Document the specific newsletter that addresses the question.

1. Refer to note below CPT code 29530. In the Professional Edition of CPT what does the following note indicate?

   → *CPT Assistant* Feb 96:3, April 02:13, Jun 10:8, Aug 10:15

   **Answer: This note refers the coder to the various editions of *CPT Assistant*.**

3. The surgeon performed a nipple-sparing mastectomy. How is this reported to distinguish this procedure from a total mastectomy?

   **Answer: All of the mastectomy procedures for cancer are reported with 19303. There are no special codes for this type of procedure. Guidance provided in *CPT Assistant*, March 2015, page 5.**

5. What is the correct code assignment for a bipolar radiofrequency hemorrhoidectomy? (*CPT Assistant,* April 2015, page 10)

   **Answer: The correct code is 46930 Destruction of internal hemorrhoid(s) by thermal energy.**

## Exercise 2.3 Application of CPT

1. The physician performs a synovial biopsy of the metacarpophalangeal joint. Using the Alphabetic Index, what key word(s) lead you to the coding selection? What is the correct code?

   **Answer (several entries in index):**

   **Synovium, Biopsy, Metacarpophalangeal Joint, with Synovial Biopsy** ................................................. **26105**
   **Biopsy, Metacarpophalangeal Joint** ....................................... **26105, 29900**
   **Metacarpophalangeal Joint, Biopsy, Synovium** .................... **26105, 29900**

   **Answer: 26105**

3. After an injection of lidocaine, the surgeon performed a percutaneous tenotomy (Achilles tendon). Refer to 27605–27606. What is the correct code assignment?

   **Answer: Lidocaine is a local anesthesia; therefore, code 27605 is assigned.**

5. Refer to codes 57550–57556. The surgeon performed an excision of a cervical stump, vaginally, with repair of an enterocele. What is the correct code assignment?

   **Answer: 57556. The description for this code would be Excision of cervical stump, vaginal approach; with repair of enterocele.**

7. Percutaneous needle biopsy of the pancreas

   **Index: Biopsy, Pancreas**

   **Code: 48102**

   **Code: 41018**

9. Laparoscopic Roux-en-Y gastric bypass procedure (150 cm)

   **Index: Roux-En-Y Procedure**

   **Code: 43644**

## Exercise 2.4 Multiple Choice Questions

1. c

3. a

5. b

7. a

9. b

# Chapter 3

# Modifiers

## Exercise 3.1: Use of Modifiers

Match the modifier with the correct description.

1. ____ 3P **(C)**

3. ____ 73 **(D)**

5. ____ 53 **(E)**

## Exercise 3.2: Select the Modifier Exercise

Read the following case scenarios and indicate the appropriate modifier.

1. A 35-year-old patient is seen in the physician's office for his yearly physical (CPT code 99395—*Preventive Medicine E/M*). During the exam, the patient requests that the physician remove a mole on his shoulder. What CPT modifier would be appended to the 99395 to explain that the E/M service was unrelated to excision of the mole?

   **Answer: Modifier 25 Significant, Separately Identifiable E/M Service on Same Day of Procedure or Other Service.**

3. A surgeon performed an esophageal dilation (43453) on a 4-week-old newborn that weighed 3.1 kg. What CPT modifier would be appended to CPT code to describe this special circumstance?

   **Answer: 63 Procedure Performed on Infants Less than 4 kg**

5. An arthroscopic meniscectomy of the knee was planned for a patient. During the procedure, the scope was inserted but the patient went into respiratory distress and the procedure was terminated. What CPT modifier would be appended to the CPT code (29880) for the physician's services?

   **Answer: 53 Discontinued Procedure. This modifier would be appended to the planned procedure for *physician services*.**

## Exercise 3.3: Coding/Modifiers

### Case Study #1

The surgeon performed a carpal tunnel release (median nerve) on the left and right wrist.

   **Index: Carpal Tunnel Syndrome, Decompression**

   **Code(s): 64721-50 (modifier for bilateral)**

### Case Study #3

The physician excised a chalazion of the left lower eyelid

**Index:  Excision, Chalazion, Single**

**Code(s): 67800-E2  Excision of chalazion; single (modifier for left lower eyelid)**

### Case Study #5

The surgeon performed a tonsillectomy and adenoidectomy on a 25-year-old male. Four hours after leaving the surgery center, the patient presents to the clinic with a one-hour history of bleeding in the throat. The bleeding site was located; however, it was in a location that could not be treated outside the OR. The patient was taken back to the OR, by the same surgeon, for control of postoperative bleeding. Code both procedures.

**Index: Tonsillectomy and Hemorrhage, Control, Throat**

**Code(s): 42821: Tonsillectomy and adenoidectomy, age 12 years or older**
**42962-78 Control oropharyngeal hemorrhage with secondary surgical intervention (modifier for return to OR for a related procedure during the postoperative period)**

## Exercise 3.4: Multiple Choice Questions

1. a

3. c

5. d

7. b

9. a

# Chapter 4

# Surgery: Part I
# Integumentary System Exercises

## Exercise 4.1: Medical Terminology Review

Match the medical terms with the definitions.

   1. ____ biopsy (**C**)

   3. ____ cryosurgery (**A**)

   5. ____ lipoma (**E**)

## Exercise 4.2: Clinical Concepts

Fill in the blanks for the following scenarios. Choose from one of the two answers provided in parentheses.

1. The 3.0 cm lipoma extended into the tendon of the shoulder. The code for this procedure would be selected from the chapter (integumentary or **musculoskeletal**).

3. The surgeon removes a 2.0 cm basal cell carcinoma of the neck. The lesion would be defined as _____ (benign or **malignant**).

5. The skin graft required harvesting healthy skin from the patient's right thigh to cover the defect of the arm. This type of graft is called: _____ (**autograft**, allograft, or xenograft).

## Exercise 4.3: Integumentary System Coding Drill

1. A surgeon reports that the patient has a 2.5 cm basal cell carcinoma of the chin. The excision required removal of 0.5 cm margins around the lesion.

   **Index: Lesion, Skin, Excision, Malignant**

   **Code(s): 11644 (size calculated as 2.5 cm + .5 cm + .5 cm = 3.5 excised diameter)**

3. A patient is seen in the Emergency Department after an accident. A 4.0 cm deep wound of the upper arm (located in area of non-muscle fascia) required a layered closure and a 1.0 cm superficial laceration of the left cheek was repaired.

   **Index: Wound, Repair, Arms, (intermediate and simple). Terms "deep, non-muscle fascia" and "layered" documents an intermediate closure. Superficial indicates a simple repair.**

   **Code(s): 12032 Intermediate repair (extremities) 2.6 to 7.5 cm**
   **12011 Simple repair, face 2.5 or less**

5. Operative Procedure: Shaving of a 0.75 cm pyogenic granuloma of the neck

   **Index: Lesion, Skin, Shaving (Note that pyogenic granuloma is a benign lesion characterized as a red papule.)**

   **Code(s): 11306 Shaving of dermal lesion, single**

7. Operative Note: Patient seeking treatment for a cyst of right breast. A 21-gauge needle was inserted into the cyst. The white, cystic fluid was aspirated and the needle withdrawn. Pressure was applied to the wound and the site covered with a bandage.

   **Index: Breast, Cyst, Puncture Aspiration**

   **Code(s): 19000-RT Puncture aspiration of cyst of breast**

9. A physician performs a simple avulsion of the nail plate, second and third digits of the right foot.

   **Index: Nails, Avulsion**

   **Code(s): 11730-T6, 11732-T7 (11732 is an add-on code used to identify each additional nail plate.)**

## Exercise 4.4: Case Studies—Integumentary System Operative and Emergency Department Reports

**1.**

### Dermatology Office Note

*Abstract from Documentation:*

What type of lesion was removed?
**Benign lesion (actinic keratosis)**

How was it removed?
**Liquid nitrogen, a form of chemical destruction**

What other documentation is needed to support the code assignment?
**The number of lesions**

🕐 *Time to Code:*

**Index: Lesion, Skin, Destruction, Benign**

**Code(s): 17000 Destruction; first lesion**

**17003 Destruction; second lesion**

**17003 Destruction; third lesion**

**3.**

**Operative Report**

✎ *Abstract from Documentation:*

What procedure was performed?
**Excision of lesion and skin graft to cover the defect**

What are the excised diameter, location, and type (malignant/benign) of lesion?
**Malignant lesion of left heel was 1.0 cm, but 2.5 cm margins were obtained
(1.5 + 2.5 + 2.5 = 6.5 cm lesion).**

What is the coding guideline for excision of lesion with subsequent skin replacement
surgery? Do you code both or just the skin graft?
**When an excision of a lesion requires a skin replacement/substitute graft for repair
of the defect, the coder should assign the excision of lesion code in addition to the
graft.**

What type of skin graft was performed? Adjacent? Skin replacement? Autograft?
Cultured tissue?
**Free (autologous) from thigh to cover defect of heel**

Was the skin graft full thickness or split thickness?
**Split thickness**

For coding purposes, identify site of defect, size, and type of graft.
**Split thickness, autograft, heel, and less than 100 sq cm (size of skin removed was
7 × 7 cm)**

🕐 *Time to Code:*

**Index for Excision of Lesion: Lesion, Skin, Excision, Malignant**

**Index for Skin Graft: Skin Graft and Flap, Split Graft**

**Code(s): 15120 Split-thickness autograft, feet, first 100 sq. cm or less
11626-59 Excision, malignant lesion, feet, over 4.0 cm**

**5.**

## Operative Report

*Abstract from Documentation:*

How was the lesion removed?
**Shaving**

Was the lesion benign or malignant?
**Nevus; benign**

What key pieces of documentation are needed for this type of treatment?
**Size (2.0 cm) and location (scalp)**

*Time to Code:*

**Index: Lesion, Skin, Shaving**

**Code(s): 11307 Shaving of epidermal lesion, 2.0 cm**

**(Note: The surgeon took a biopsy of the lesion to send to Pathology. CPT guidelines state that if a biopsy and removal is performed on the same lesion, only code the removal.)**

# Musculoskeletal System Exercises

## Exercise 4.5: Crossword Puzzle

**Across**

3. Bones of hand [METACARPAL]
5. Near center of body [PROXIMAL]
6. Cartilage in knee joint [MENISCUS]
7. Knee bone [PATELLA]

**Down**

1. Away from center of body [DISTAL]
2. Bone of upper arm [HUMERUS]
4. Bones of fingers or toes [PHALANGES]

## Exercise 4.6: Clinical Concepts

Fill in the blanks to the following scenarios. Choose from one of the two answers provided in parentheses.

1. The radiology report revealed that the displaced fracture did not heal. This fracture would be referred to as _____ (**nonunion** or malunion).

3. The patient has advanced arthritis of the elbow joint. The physician performs a fusion of the joint to provide stability. This procedure is referred to as _____ (**arthrodesis**, tenolysis).

5. The talus bone is located in the _____ (knee, **ankle**).

## Exercise 4.7: Musculoskeletal System Coding Drill

Review the documentation and underline key term(s). Identify the terms used to look up the code selection in the Alphabetic Index. Assign CPT codes to the following cases. If applicable, append CPT modifiers.

1. A patient is diagnosed with osteochondroma of the right clavicle. The surgeon excises the tumor.

   **Index: Tumor, Clavicle, Excision (Osteochondroma is benign)**

   **Code(s): 23140 Excision or curettage of bone cyst or benign tumor of clavicle or scapula**

3. The surgeon performed a percutaneous tenotomy of the left hand, second digit and third digit.

   **Index: Tenotomy, finger**

   **Code(s): 26060-F1 and 26060-F2**

5. The patient had been diagnosed with an infected abscess extending below the fascia of the knee. The surgeon performed an incision and drainage of the abscess.

   **Index: Incision and Drainage, knee**

   **Code(s): 27301 Incision and drainage, deep abscess, bursa, or hematoma, thigh or knee region**

7. The surgeon performed a closed reduction of a scapular fracture.

   **Index: Fracture, Scaphoid, Closed Treatment**

   **Code(s): 25624 Closed treatment of carpal scaphoid (navicular) fracture, with reduction**

9. Patient treated for posttraumatic osteoarthritis of right knee. The surgeon performed a total knee arthroplasty. All components were removed and surfaces were irrigated. The components were cemented into place beginning with a femoral component and followed by the tibial component and then the patellar component.

   **Index: Replacement, Knee**

   **Code(s): 27447-RT Arthroplasty, knee, total**

## Exercise 4.8: Case Studies—Musculoskeletal System Operative and Emergency Department Reports

**1.**

### Emergency Department Record

*Abstract from Documentation:*

What is the location of the fracture?
**Distal fibula**

What services did the Emergency Department physician perform?
**Closed treatment of distal fibular fracture**

🕐 *Time to Code:*

**Index: Fracture, Fibula, Closed Treatment**

**Code(s): 27788-RT Closed treatment of distal fibular fracture with manipulation**

**3.**

### Operative Report

*Abstract from Documentation:*

What is a K-wire?
**Pin fixation to hold bone fragments together**

What procedure was performed for this patient?
**Removal of pin**

🕐 *Time to Code:*

**Index: Removal, Fixation Device**

**Code(s): 20680 Removal of implant; deep (buried pin)**

**5.**

### Operative Report

*Abstract from Documentation:*

What is a trigger finger?
**A trigger finger occurs when the motion of the tendon that opens and closes the finger is limited, causing the finger to lock or catch as the finger is extended.**

What was performed to correct the condition?
**Flexor tendon sheath was divided (incision into tendon sheath)**

*Time to Code:*

**Index: Finger, Tendon, Sheath, Incision**

**Code(s): 26055-F2 Tendon sheath incision**

# Respiratory System Exercises

## Exercise 4.9: Medical Terminology Review

Match the following terms with the correct definition.

1. _____ larynx (**E**)

3. _____ bronchus (**A**)

5. _____ ethmoid (**D**)

## Exercise 4.10: Clinical Concepts

Fill in the blanks to the following scenarios. Choose from one of the two answers provided in parentheses.

1. A patient is suspected of a lesion on the vocal cord. The physician would most likely perform a _____ for further diagnosis and/or treatment (**laryngoscopy**, bronchoscopy).

3. The patient has pleural fluid that must be removed. The physician would most likely perform a _____ to remove the fluid (**pneumocentesis**, pneumonectomy).

5. A patient is seen in the Emergency Department for epistaxis, and the physician performs cautery. The purpose of this procedure is to _____ (remove the nasal blockage, **control nasal hemorrhage**).

## Exercise 4.11: Respiratory System Coding Drill

Review the documentation and underline key term(s). Identify the terms used to look up the code selection in the Alphabetic Index. Assign CPT codes to the following cases. If applicable, assign CPT/HCPCS Level II modifiers.

1.  Surgeon performs an endoscopic anterior ethmoidectomy.

    **Index: Endoscopy, Nose, Surgical**

    **Code(s): 31254 Endoscopy with partial ethmoidectomy**

3.  A patient is seen in the Emergency Department for epistaxis. Physician performs an anterior packing of left nasal passage.

    **Index: Hemorrhage, Control, Nasal, Simple**

    **Code(s): 30901-LT Control nasal hemorrhage, anterior, simple**

5.  A patient is seen with difficulty breathing due to deviated nasal septum. The surgeon performs a submucous resection of the septum.

    **Index: Nasal Septum, Submucous Resection (Resection directs coder to see Nasal Septum.)**

    **Code(s): 30520 Septoplasty or submucous resection**

7.  A patient was diagnosed with squamous cell carcinoma of the larynx. The surgeon performed a supraglottic laryngectomy with radical neck dissection to remove the metastasis to the lymph nodes.

    **Index: Laryngectomy, Subtotal (Supraglottic procedure preserves part of the voice box.)**

    **Code(s): 31368 Laryngectomy; subtotal supraglottic, with radical neck dissection**

9.  With the use of an operating microscope, the surgeon performs a direct laryngoscopy for removal of a piece of a toothpick.

    **Index: Laryngoscopy, Direct, Removal, Foreign Body**

    **Code(s): 31531 Laryngoscopy, direct with foreign body removal with operating microscope**

## Exercise 4.12: Case Studies—Respiratory System Operative Reports

### 1.

**Operative Report**

*Abstract from Documentation:*

What type of endoscopy was performed?
**Bronchoscopy**

What was performed during the endoscopic procedure?
**Brush specimens and bronchial washings**

*Time to Code:*

**Index: Bronchoscopy, Brushings**

**Code(s): 31623 Bronchoscopy, with brushings (Note that cell washings are included in 31622, which is designated as a "separate procedure" code. Cell washings would be integral to 31623.)**

### 3.

**Operative Report**

*Abstract from Documentation:*

What type of endoscopy was performed?
**Laryngoscopy**

What was performed during the endoscopic procedure?
**Excision of mucoid mass and excision of cyst (For coding purpose, these are referred to as "tumors"—generic term for growths.)**

*Time to Code:*

**Index: Laryngoscopy, Operative**

**Code(s): 31541 Laryngoscopy, direct, operative with operating microscope (Only coded once even though more than one cyst was removed. Note the physician used an operating microscope.)**

**5.**

**Operative Report**

✎ *Abstract from Documentation:*

What is pleurodesis?
**It is a method to drain the fluid. In the case of a mechanical pleurodesis, the pleura is irritated with a scratch pad and fluid removed.**

🕐 *Time to Code:*

**Index: Pleurodesis, Thoracoscopic**

**Code(s): 32650 Thoracoscopy, surgical; with pleurodesis (e.g., mechanical or chemical)**

# Cardiovascular System Exercises

## Exercise 4.13: Medical Terminology Review

Match the following terms with the correct definition.

1. ____ fistula **(C)**

3. ____ stenosis **(E)**

5. ____ ligation **(A)**

## Exercise 4.14: Clinical Concepts

Fill in the blanks to the following scenarios. Choose from one of the two answers provided in parentheses.

1. A venous access device that is inserted in the cephalic vein and the tip rests in superior vena cava would be classified as _____ (centrally inserted, **peripherally inserted**).

3. A direct arteriovenous (AV) anastomosis connects the radial artery to the _____ (**cephalic vein**, inferior vena cava).

5. Central venous access devices are often used on patients who require _____ (angioplasty, **chemotherapy**).

## Exercise 4.15: Cardiovascular System Coding Drill

Review the documentation and underline key term(s). Identify the terms used to look up the code selection in the Alphabetic Index. Assign CPT codes to the following cases. If applicable, append CPT/HCPCS Level II modifiers.

1. The surgeon repairs a ruptured aneurysm of the splenic artery.

   **Index: Aneurysm Repair, Splenic Artery**

   **Code(s): 35112 Direct repair of aneurysm; for ruptured aneurysm, splenic artery**

3. Operative Note:

   Diagnosis:  Thrombosis of right AV (Gore-Tex) graft

   Procedure: A transverse incision was made in order to complete a thrombectomy of the graft. Because the balloon catheter could not be passed, it was elected to perform an arteriotomy for removal of the thrombus. The area was irrigated and the incision was closed.

   **Index: Thrombectomy, Arteriovenous Fistula, Graft leads to a percutaneous thrombectomy code. This is an open approach since the arteriotomy was performed. See in index: Thrombectomy, Dialysis Graft.**

   > **TIP: Many experienced coders rely mainly on the index to provide the range of codes and do not focus on locating the exact index entry.**

   **Code(s): 36831 Thrombectomy, open, arteriovenous fistula without revision**

5. A surgeon performs a percutaneous transluminal angioplasty on the left femoral-popliteal artery for a patient with peripheral artery disease.

   **Index: Angioplasty, Popliteal Artery, Intraoperative (Note that femoral artery leads to the same code.)**

   **Code(s): 37224-LT Revascularization, endovascular, open or percutaneous, femoral/popliteal artery(s), unilateral; with transluminal angioplasty**

7. A surgeon performed a triple coronary artery bypass using a saphenous vein.

   **Index: Coronary Artery Bypass Graft (CABG), Venous Bypass**

   **Code(s): 33512 Coronary artery bypass, vein only; three coronary venous grafts**

9. Percutaneous transcatheter placement of stent in femoral artery.

   **Index: Revascularization, Artery, Femoral/Popliteal**

   **Code(s): 37226 Revascularization, endovascular, open or percutaneous, femoral, popliteal artery(s), unilateral; with transluminal stent placement(s) includes angioplasty within the same vessel, when performed.**

## Exercise 4.16: Case Studies—Cardiovascular System Operative Reports

**1.**

### Operative Note

*Abstract from Documentation:*

What is the coding selection for a permanent pacemaker?
**Review of the index reveals the selection as 33206–33208.**

What documentation determines the correct code selection?
**If insertion is in the atrium, ventricle, or both. In this case it is both.**

*Time to Code:*

**Index: Insertion, Pacemaker Heart**

**Code(s): 33208 Insertion, atrial and ventricular**

**3.**

### Operative Report

*Abstract from Documentation:*

Review CPT notes preceding the coding section for central venous access procedures.
What is a Port-a-Cath?
**Venous access device**

What was the operative action?
**The port was removed.**

*Time to Code:*

**Index: Removal, Venous Access Device**

**Code(s): 36590 Removal of tunneled central venous access device with subcutaneous port**

**5.**

### Operative Report

*Abstract from Documentation:*

What main procedure was performed?
**Repair of stenosis**

What technique was used to eliminate the stenosis?
**Balloon angioplasty**

*Time to Code:*

**Index**: **Angioplasty, Iliac Artery, Intraoperative**

**Code(s)**: **37220-RT Revascularization, endovascular, open or percutaneous, iliac artery, unilateral, initial vessel; with transluminal angioplasty**

# Digestive System Exercises

## Exercise 4.17: Crossword Puzzle

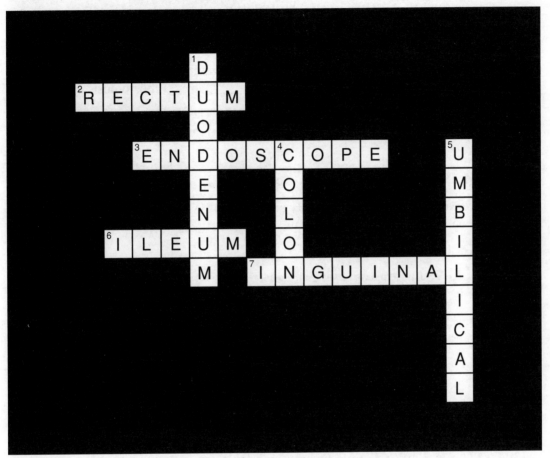

### Across

2. Final section of large intestine [RECTUM]
3. Instrument to view inside body [ENDOSCOPE]
6. Third portion of small intestines [ILEUM]
7. Groin [INGUINAL]

### Down

1. First part of small intestine [DUODENUM]
4. From cecum to rectum [COLON]
5. Navel [UMBILICAL]

### Exercise 4.18: Clinical Concepts

Fill in the blanks to the following scenarios. Choose from one of the two answers provided in parentheses.

1.  The scope was introduced through the mouth and advanced to the second portion of the duodenum. Cannulation of the common bile duct was accomplished. The common bile duct and intrahepatics were normal. This operative note describes an _____ (EGD, **ERCP**).

3.  The physician removed part of the intestine, which required surgical connection of the two ends. This procedure is called a(n) _____ (**anastomosis**, fistulotomy).

5.  The patient presents with adhesions in the intestines. The physician performs an _____ to correct the condition (enteroenterostomy, **enterolysis**).

### Exercise 4.19: Digestive System Coding Drill

1.  Operative Note: The patient is morbidly obese with a BMI of 37. Procedure performed: Laparoscopic vertical sleeve gastrectomy.

    **Index: Gastrectomy, Sleeve**

    **Code(s): 43775 Laparoscopy, surgical, gastric restrictive procedure; longitudinal gastrectomy (i.e., sleeve gastrectomy)**

3.  A patient is diagnosed with papillomas of the anus. Using cryosurgery, the surgeon removes the three papillomas.

    **Index: Lesion, Anal, Destruction**

    **Code(s): 46916 Destruction of lesions, anus, cryosurgery**

5.  The patient suffered a perforation of the pharynx wall from a bottle cap. The surgeon performed a suture repair of the wound.

    **Index: Throat, Suture, Wound (No direct index entry under Pharynx.)**

    **Code(s): 42900 Suture pharynx for wound or injury**

7.  The surgeon performed a laparoscopic repair of paraesophageal hernia.

    **Index: Laparoscopy, Hernia Repair, Paraesophageal**

    **Code(s): 43281 Laparoscopy, surgical, repair of paraesophageal hernia**

9.  The surgeon performed an esophagoscopy (flexible, transoral) for removal of a polyp via hot biopsy forceps.

    **Index: Esophagoscopy, Transoral, Removal, Polyp**

    **Code(s): 43216 Esophagoscopy with removal of polyp by hot biopsy forceps**

## Exercise 4.20: Case Studies—Digestive System Operative and Emergency Department Reports

### 1.

**Operative Report**

*Abstract from Documentation:*

Was this a diagnostic or surgical colonoscopy?
**Surgical**

What technique was used to remove the polyp?
**Snare**

*Time to Code:*

**Index: Colonoscopy, Proximal to Splenic Flexure, with Removal, Tumor**

**Code(s): 45385 Colonoscopy with removal by snare technique**

### 3.

**Emergency Department Record**

*Abstract from Documentation:*

What type of endoscopy was performed?
**Esophagoscopy**

What procedure was performed during the endoscopy?
**Removal of foreign body**

*Time to Code:*

**Index: Endoscopy, Esophagus, Removal, Foreign Body**

**Code(s): 43215 Esophagoscopy with removal of foreign body**

## 5.

**Operative Report**

*Abstract from Documentation:*

What method was used to remove the hemorrhoids?
**Excision**

Where the hemorrhoids internal or external?
**External**

How many columns or groups were documented?
**Three**

*Time to Code:*

**Index: Hemorrhoid, Excision—See Hemorrhoidectomy
   Hemorrhoidectomy, External Complete**

**Code(s): 46250 Hemorrhoidectomy, external, two or more columns/groups**

## 7.

**Operative Report**

*Abstract from Documentation:*

Locate the code selection for colectomy. What additional information is needed from the operative report to assign a correct code?
**Partial or total and additional procedures**

In the index, what code selection is provided for the liver biopsy?
**47000, 47001, 47100**

How are the codes differentiated?
**Percutaneous, performed at time of major procedure, and if wedge biopsy was performed**

*Time to Code:*

**Index: #1-Colectomy, Partial with Anastomosis
   #2-Biopsy, Liver**

**Code(s): 44140 Colectomy, partial; with anastomosis
   47001 Biopsy of liver, needle; when done for indicated purpose at time of other major procedure (List separately in addition to code for primary procedure.)**

# Chapter 4

# Surgery: Part II
# Urinary System Exercises

## Exercise 4.21: Medical Terminology Review

Match the medical terms with the correct definitions.

1. ____ lith (**D**)
3. ____ bladder (**A**)
5. ____ urethra (**B**)

## Exercise 4.22: Clinical Concepts

Fill in the blanks for the following scenarios. Choose from one of the two answers provided in parentheses.

1. Which of the following procedures would use sound waves to break up a ureteral stone? (**lithotripsy**, cystopexy)

3. The surgeon inserts a telescope-like tube into the bladder from the natural orifice to visualize the lower urinary tract. This procedure is referred to as a(n) _____ (**cystourethroscopy**, ERCP).

5. Which of the following procedures would be performed for urinary stress incontinence? (**urethral suspension**, cystorrhaphy)

## Exercise 4.23: Urinary System Coding Drill

For all coding exercises, review the documentation and underline key term(s). Identify the terms used to look up the code selection in the Alphabetic Index. Assign CPT codes to the following cases. If applicable, append CPT/HCPCS Level II modifiers. In some cases, the student will be prompted to answer questions about the case study.

1. The surgeon performs a laparoscopic ablation of a renal cyst.

   **Index: Cyst, Kidney, Ablation**

   **Code(s): 50541 Laparoscopy, ablation of renal cyst**

3. Operative Note: Patient has a ureteral stricture. Performed a cystoscopy with ureteroscopy and laser treatment of the stricture.

   **Index: Cystourethroscopy, Dilation, Ureter**

   **Code(s): 52344 Cystourethroscopy with ureteroscopy; with treatment of ureteral stricture**

5. The surgeon aspirates the cyst of the kidney with the use of a percutaneous needle.

   **Index: Kidney, Cyst, Aspiration**

   **Code(s): 50390 Aspiration and/or injection of renal cyst by needle, percutaneous**

7. Percutaneous nephrostolithotomy for basket extraction of 1.5 cm stone

   **Index: Nephrostolithotomy**

   **Code(s): 50080 Percutaneous nephrostolithotomy; 1.5 cm stone**

9. Percutaneous needle biopsy of the kidney

   **Index: Biopsy, Kidney**

   **Code(s): 50200 Renal biopsy; percutaneous, by trocar or needle**

## Exercise 4.24: Case Studies—Urinary System Operative Reports

**1.**

### Operative Report

*Abstract from Documentation:*

What is meant by the "urethra was then calibrated"?
**The diameter of the urethra was measured.**

*Time to Code:*

**Index: Cystourethroscopy, Dilation, Urethra**

**Code(s): 52281 Cystourethroscopy, with calibration and/or dilation of urethral stricture or stenosis (can be male or female)**

**3.**

## Operative Report

*Abstract from Documentation:*

How were the stones removed?
**Via shock wave lithotripsy (Stone was treated with 3,000 shocks.)**

*Time to Code:*

**Index: Lithotripsy, Kidney**

**Code(s): 50590 Lithotripsy, extracorporeal shock wave**

**5.**

## Operative Report

*Abstract from Documentation:*

What was visualized during the endoscopy procedure?
**Urethra to bladder**

*Time to Code:*

**Index: Cystourethroscopy**

**Code(s): 52000 Cystourethroscopy (separate procedure)**

# Male Genital System Exercises

### Exercise 4.25: Medical Terminology Review

Match the medical terms with the definitions.

1. ____ epididymis (**E**)

3. ____ testicles (**A**)

5. ____ circumcision (**D**)

### Exercise 4.26: Clinical Concepts

Fill in the blanks for the following scenarios. Choose from one of the two answers provided in parentheses.

1. The male patient is seeking a sterilization procedure to prevent the release of sperm. This procedure is referred to as _____ (orchiectomy, **vasectomy**).

3. A patient has been diagnosed with undescended testis. Which of the following procedures would correct this condition? (urethroplasty, **orchiopexy**)

### Exercise 4.27: Male Genital System Coding Drill

1. The surgeon performs a 1-stage distal hypospadias repair with urethroplasty using local skin flaps.

   **Index: Hypospadias, Urethroplasty, Local Skin Flaps**

   **Code(s): 54324 1-stage distal hypospadias repair with urethroplasty by local skin flaps**

3. The patient has a history of azoospermia. The surgeon performs bilateral open testicular biopsies.

   **Index: Biopsy, Testis**

   **Code(s): 54505-50**
   **The note under code 54505 directs coders to assign modifier 50 if the procedure is bilateral.**

5. Patient is a 55-year-old male with a Mentor inflatable three-piece penile prosthesis that had been causing problems. He was experiencing issues with prolonged erections while deflating the prosthesis. It was elected to remove the prosthesis and insert a Duraphase II penile prosthesis. There was some evidence of infection in the area, which was irrigated.

   **Index: Removal, Prosthesis, Penis**

   **Code(s): 54411 Removal and replacement of all components of a multi-component inflatable penile prosthesis through an infected field at the same operative session, including irrigation and debridement of infected tissue**

## Exercise 4.28: Case Studies—Male Genital System Operative Reports

### 1.

**Operative Report**

✎ *Abstract from Documentation:*

Review the Alphabetic Index for the coding selection for Prostatectomy. What documentation would be needed to choose the range to verify?
**Laparoscopic, Perineal, Retropubic, Suprapubic, or Transurethral**
**Also, for perineal/retropubic and suprapubic, the coder must determine if the procedure was partial or radical.**

🕐 *Time to Code:*

**Index: Prostatectomy, Retropubic, Radical (55840–55845, 55866)**

**Code(s): 55845 Prostatectomy, retropubic radical, with or without nerve sparing; with bilateral pelvic lymphadenectomy**

### 3.

**Operative Report**

✎ *Abstract from Documentation:*

What technique was used to obtain the biopsy?
**Needle**

🕐 *Time to Code:*

**Index: Biopsy, Prostate**

**Code(s): 55700 Biopsy, prostate; needle or punch, single or multiple, any approach**

# Female Genital System Exercises

## Exercise 4.29: Medical Terminology Review

Match the following medical terms with the correct definition.

1. ____ cervix (**D**)
3. ____ ovary (**B**)
5. ____ laparoscopy (**A**)

## Exercise 4.30: Clinical Concepts

Fill in the blanks for the following scenarios. Choose from one of the two answers provided in parentheses.

1. As a result of a positive Pap smear, the surgeon recommends a _____ to determine the cause (laparoscopy, **colposcopy**).

3. The surgeon excised extensive adhesions that encased the ovary. Freeing of adhesions is known as _____ (ligation, **lysis**).

5. Which of the following procedures would be associated with removal of uterine fibroids? (**myomectomy**, cerclage of uterine cervix)

## Exercise 4.31: Female Genital System Coding Drill

1. The surgeon performs an incision and drainage of vulvar abscess

   **Index: Incision and Drainage, Abscess, Vulva**

   **Code(s): 56405 Incision and drainage of vulva abscess**

3. Operative Note: Patient has chronic complaints of right pelvic pain. Taken to OR for a laparoscopy. Inspection into the pelvis revealed multiple adhesions attached to the left tube and ovary. These adhesions were lysed bluntly with probe. No other abnormalities noted.

   **Index: Laparoscopy, Lysis of Adhesions**

   **Code(s): 58660 Laparoscopy, surgical; with lysis of adhesions**

5. The OB/GYN physician delivers a baby via Cesarean section. The physician has provided all obstetrical care prior to delivery and will continue to follow the patient for her postpartum care.

What coding guidelines pertain to maternity care and are applicable in this case?
**Code 59510 would be reported by a physician providing global care for a Cesarean delivery.**

**Index: Cesarean Delivery, Routine Care**

**Code(s): 59510 Routine obstetric care including antepartum care, Cesarean delivery, and postpartum care**

## Exercise 4.32: Case Studies—Female Genital System Operative Reports

**1.**

### Operative Report

✎ *Abstract from Documentation:*

Refer to the key term Hysterectomy in the Alphabetic Index. What key documentation is needed to lead to the correct coding range?
**Vaginal and then Laparoscopic drives the coding range. After the range of codes is identified and verified, other key documentation is needed (for example, size of uterus, removal of tubes and ovaries).**

🕐 *Time to Code:*

**Index: Hysterectomy, Vaginal, Removal Tubes/Ovaries**

**Code(s): 58552 Laparoscopic, surgical, with vaginal hysterectomy, for uterus 250 g or less with removal of tube(s) and ovary(s)**

**3.**

### Operative Report

✎ *Abstract from Documentation:*

Refer to the key term in the Alphabetic Index. What information is needed to assign a CPT code for this procedure?
**Whether it was performed laparoscopically or not**

🕐 *Time to Code:*

**Index: Tubal Ligation (58600)**

**Code(s): 58600 Ligation or transection of fallopian tube(s) abdominal or vaginal approach, unilateral or bilateral**

**5.**

### Operative Note

*Abstract from Documentation:*

Review the Alphabetic Index for coding selections for vulvectomy procedures. What documentation is needed for the coding selection?
**Complete, Partial, Radical, Simple**

Note the definitions for simple, radical, partial, and complete vulvectomy codes (listed before code 56405). What documentation from this operative note leads you to the correct definition?
**Physician dictates that the vulvectomy was partial (removes less than 80 percent of vulvar area).**

Was this a *radical* (removal of skin and deep subcutaneous tissue) or *simple* (removal of skin and superficial subcutaneous tissue) procedure?
**The term "undermined" (dig beneath) implies that it was beyond the superficial subcutaneous tissues. It may be a good step to query the physician in this case.**

*Time to Code:*

**Index: Vulvectomy, partial (56620, 56630–56632)**

**Code(s): 56630 Vulvectomy, radical, partial**

# Nervous System Exercises

## Exercise 4.33: Medical Terminology Review

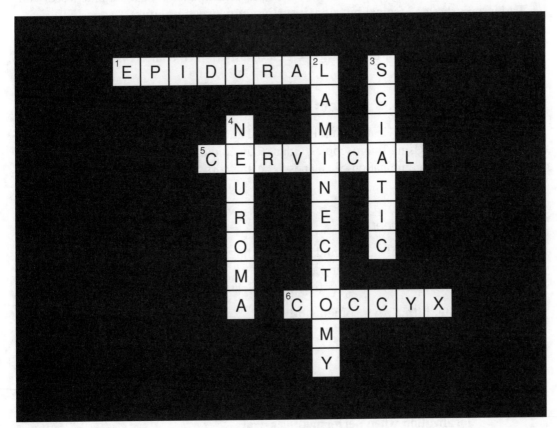

**Across**

1. Space around dura mater in spinal cord [EPIDURAL]
5. Vertebra of neck [CERVICAL]
6. Base of spine [COCCYX]

**Down**

2. Surgical removal of vertebrae [LAMINECTOMY]
3. Major nerve runs back of thigh [SCIATIC]
4. Tumor of nerves [NEUROMA]

## Exercise 4.34: Clinical Concepts

Fill in the blanks to the following scenarios. Choose from one of the two answers provided in parentheses.

1.  Which of the following procedures would be performed to treat a patient diagnosed with Parkinson's disease? (spinal infusion, **insertion of neurostimulator**)

3.  Surgical treatment of carpal tunnel syndrome would be documented as _____ (**release compression of median nerve**, neuroplasty of median nerve).

## Exercise 4.35: Nervous System Coding Drill

1.  Operative Note for Cervical Epidural Injection: Patient has been experiencing neck pain for several years. Using fluoroscopic guidance, an epidural needle is inserted into the epidural space. A combination of an anesthetic and cortisone steroid solution is injected into the epidural space.

    *Abstract from Documentation:*

    Refer to Basic CPT/HCPCS for guidance on coding for spinal injections. What documentation is needed for coding selection?
    **Site of injection and substance (site is cervical, substance is anesthetic and steroid)**

    **Useful website: http://www.spine-health.com**

    *Time to Code:*

    **Index: Injection, Spinal Cord, Anesthetic 62310–62319**

    **Code(s): 62310 Injection, (including anesthetic, steroid) includes contrast for localization when performed; cervical**

3.  The surgeon sutures a lacerated digital nerve of the left hand, a result of injury.

    **Index: Suture, Nerve**

    **Code(s): 64831-LT Suture of digital nerve, hand or foot, one nerve**

5.  Under imaging guidance, the patient undergoes an epidural injection of a neurolytic agent at the L5 joint.

    **Index: Epidural, Injection**

    **Code(s): 62282 Injection of neurolytic substance; lumbar**

7.  Operative Note: Patient has lumbar stenosis at L3–4 and L4–5. Surgeon performed a right partial L3 and partial L4 hemilaminectomy with undermining laminotomy for decompression of nerve roots.

    **Index: Hemilaminectomy 63020–63044**

    **Code(s): 63030 Laminotomy (hemilaminectomy)—one interspace, lumbar
    63035 each additional interspace**

9. Patient was diagnosed with a subdural hematoma. The surgeon created two left-sided burr holes for evacuation of the blood.

**Index: Burr Hole, Skull, for Drainage, Hematoma**

**Code(s): 61154 Burr hole(s) with evacuation and drainage of hematoma, subdural**

## Exercise 4.36: Case Studies—Nervous System Operative Reports

**1.**

### Operative Report

*Abstract from Documentation:*

What is a spinal cord stimulator?
**Also called neurostimulator, it is an implantable device often used to treat chronic pain. The pulse generator holds the batteries; therefore, replacement of batteries codes as replacement of pulse generator.**

*Time to Code:*

**Index: Replacement, Neurostimulator, Pulse Generator/Receiver, Spinal**

**Code(s): 63685 Insertion or replacement of spinal neurostimulator pulse generator**

**3.**

### Operative Report

*Abstract from Documentation:*

What procedure was performed (key operative term)?
**Decompression**

What is the location of the nerve entrapment?
**Left ulnar nerve**

*Time to Code:*

**Index: Nerves, Decompression**

**Code(s): 64718-LT Neuroplasty; ulnar nerve at elbow**

**5.**

## Operative Report

*Abstract from Documentation:*

Refer to *Basic CPT/HCPCS* for coding guidance. What is a discectomy?
**A discectomy is a surgery done to remove a herniated disc from the spine. A laminectomy is often involved to permit access to the intervertebral disc.**

After the location of the curette was confirmed, what was the first surgical action?
**Lamina was partially drilled off (hemilaminectomy).**
**Refer to this term in the Alphabetic Index.**

*Time to Code:*

**Index: Hemilaminectomy**

**Code(s): 63030 Laminotomy (hemilaminectomy) with decompression of nerve root(s), including foraminotomy and/or excision of herniated intervertebral disc; one interspace, lumbar**

**An interactive video of this procedure can be found at http://www.spine-health.com.**

# Eye and Ocular Adnexa Exercises

**Exercise 4.37: Medical Terminology Review**

**Across**

2. Cyst of eyelid [CHALAZION]
3. Opening of tear duct [PUNCTUM]
5. Drooping of eyelids [PTOSIS]
6. Eyes deviate outward [EXOTROPIA]
7. Benign growth of conjunctiva [PTERYGIUM]

**Down**

1. Inner part of eyelid [CONJUNCTIVA]
4. Abnormal alignment of eyes [STRABISMUS]

## Exercise 4.38: Clinical Concepts

Fill in the blanks to the following scenarios. Choose from one of the two answers provided in parentheses.

1. A patient is diagnosed with crossed eyes. Which of the following procedures would be performed to correct this condition? (vitrectomy, **strabismus surgery**)

3. Which of the following procedures is associated with treatment of retinal detachment? (**scleral buckling**, keratoplasty)

5. The patient is seeking treatment for extreme dry eyes. Which of the following procedures would be used to treat this condition? (**insertion of punctal plugs**, phacoemulsification)

## Exercise 4.39: Eye and Ocular Adnexa Coding Drill

1. Patient diagnosed with exotropia. Surgeon performs bilateral recession of lateral rectus muscles.

*Abstract from Documentation:*

What is the definition of exotropia?
**Type of strabismus in which the eyes are turned outward**

Refer to *Basic CPT/HCPCS*: How is the lateral rectus muscle classified (vertical or horizontal)?
**Horizontal**

*Time to Code:*

**Index: Strabismus, Repair, One Horizontal Muscle**

**Code(s): 67311-50 Strabismus surgery, recession or resection procedure; one horizontal muscle**

3. Incision and drainage of abscess of the upper right eyelid

**Index: Incision and Drainage, Abscess, Eyelid**

**Code(s): 67700-E3 Blepharotomy, drainage of abscess, eyelid**

5. Under general anesthesia, the surgeon probes the nasolacrimal ducts with irrigation, bilaterally.

**Index: Nasolacrimal Duct, Exploration, with Anesthesia**

**Code(s): 68811-50 Probing of nasolacrimal duct requiring general anesthesia**

## Exercise 4.40: Case Studies—Eye and Ocular Adnexa Operative and Emergency Department Reports

**1.**

### Operative Report

*Abstract from Documentation:*

Refer to the key operative term in the Alphabetic Index and note the code range.

What documentation is needed from the record to correctly assign a CPT code(s)? **Determine whether the procedure was performed on the upper or lower eyelids (unilateral or bilateral). Next, note that the diagnostic information contributes to the coding in this case (excessive skin weighting down lid).**

**The blepharoplasty codes appear in the Integumentary System section. More extensive eyelid repair codes appear in the Eye and Ocular Adnexa section (e.g., 67901).**

*Time to Code:*

**Index: Blepharoplasty**

**Code(s): 15823-50 Blepharoplasty; upper eyelid; with excessive skin weighting down lid**

**3.**

### Emergency Department Record

*Abstract from Documentation:*

Why did the patient seek treatment in the Emergency Department?
**Foreign body in eye**

What procedure (and technique) was performed?
**Removal of foreign body of cornea with use of slit lamp**

*Time to Code:*

**Index: Removal, Foreign Body, Cornea with Slit Lamp**

**Code(s): 65222-RT Removal of foreign body, external eye; corneal, with slit lamp**

# Auditory System Exercises

## Exercise 4.41: Medical Terminology Review

Match the following terms with the correct definition.

1. ____ myringotomy **(C)**
3. ____ stapedectomy **(D)**
5. ____ tympanum **(B)**

## Exercise 4.42: Clinical Concepts

Fill in the blanks to the following scenarios. Choose from one of the two answers provided in parentheses.

1. The patient is seen for chronic middle ear infection. Conservative treatment with antibiotics would not clear the infection, so it was elected to perform a(n) _____ to remove the infection (**mastoidectomy**, otoplasty).

3. Which of the following procedures is associated with reconstructive surgery of the eardrum? (**tympanoplasty**, otoplasty)

## Exercise 4.43: Auditory System Coding Drill

1. Physician Office Note

   Examination of the ear canal on both sides revealed impacted cerumen, tightly on the right side and a little bit on the left. With the use of ear curette, the impacted cerumen was removed. Both ears were irrigated with saline solution and suctioned dry to clean out all the debris.

   **Index: Cerumen, Removal**

   **Code(s): 69210-50 Removal of impacted cerumen, one or both ears**

3. The surgeon performs a bilateral otoplasty for the patient's protruding ears.

   **Index: Otoplasty**

   **Code(s): 69300-50 Otoplasty, protruding ear, with or without size reduction**

## Exercise 4.44: Case Studies—Auditory Operative Reports

**1.**

### Operative Report

*Abstract from Documentation:*

Refer to *Basic CPT/HCPCS* for guidelines pertaining to myringotomy for insertion of tubes. What coding guidance is provided in the textbook for this procedure?
**Select code from tympanostomy range.**

*Time to Code:*

**Index: Tympanostomy, General Anesthesia**

**Code(s): 69436-50 Tympanostomy (requiring insertion of ventilating tube), general anesthesia**

**3.**

### Operative Report

*Abstract from Documentation:*

What is a stapedectomy?
**Surgeon removes a portion of bone and places prosthesis to transmit the sound.**

*Time to Code:*

**Index: Stapes, Excision, with Footplate Drill Out**

**Code(s): 69661-LT Stapedectomy or stapedotomy with reestablishment of ossicular continuity, with or without use of foreign material; with footplate drill out**

## Exercise 4.45: Multiple Choice Questions

1. a
3. b
5. d
7. c
9. d

# Chapter 5

# Radiology

## Exercise 5.1: Medical Terminology Review

1. _____ CT scan (**B**)
3. _____ MRI (**C**)
5. _____ X-ray (**A**)

## Exercise 5.2: Case Studies

### Case Study #1

**MRI Scan of the Pelvis**

**Index: Magnetic Resonance Imaging, Pelvis**

**Code: 72197 Magnetic resonance imaging, pelvis; without contrast material, followed by contrast material and further sequences**

### Case Study #3

**Oral Cholecystogram**

**Index: Cholecystography**

**Code(s): 74290 Cholecystography, oral contrast**

### Case Study #5

**KUB, Upper GI Series**

**Index: X-ray, Gastrointestinal Tract**

**Code(s): 74241 Radiological examination, gastrointestinal tract, upper; with or without delayed films, with KUB**

### Case Study #7

**Bilateral Screening Mammogram**

**Index: Mammography, Screening**

**Code(s): 77057 Screening mammography, bilateral**

## Case Study #9

**General Radiology**

**Chest, 2 Views**

**Index: X-ray, Chest**

**Code(s): 71020 Radiologic examination, chest, 2 views, frontal and lateral**

## Case Study #11

**KUB and Intravenous Pyelogram**

**Index: Pyelography**

**Code(s): 74400 Urography (pyelography), intravenous, with or without KUB, with or without tomography**

## Exercise 5.3: Multiple Choice Questions

1. c
3. d
5. b
7. c
9. a

# Chapter 6

# Pathology and Laboratory

## Exercise 6.1: Case Studies

### Case Study #1

**GENERAL CHEMISTRY**

| Sodium | Potassium | Chloride | Total CO$_2$ | Glucose | BUN | Creatinine | Ionized Calcium |
|--------|-----------|----------|--------------|---------|-----|------------|-----------------|
| 138 | 3.3 | 96 | 34 | 104 | 20 | 0.8 | 6.0 |

**Index: Organ or Disease-Oriented Panel, Metabolic, Basic**

**Code(s): 80047 Basic Metabolic Panel**

### Case Study #3

An 8-year-old girl presents in the urgent care center for abdominal pain associated with some diarrhea. The physician orders a fecal calprotectin test.

**Index: Calprotectin, Fecal**

**Code(s): 83993 Calprotectin, fecal**

### Case Study #5

Pathology Report
Specimen: Prostate chips from TURP

**Index: Pathology and Laboratory, Surgical Pathology, Gross and Micro Exam**

**Code(s): 88305 Level IV (Note: Level IV is appropriate because the prostate was received in "chips," meaning that it was removed in a transurethral manner.)**

### Case Study #7

**Lipid Panel**

| Test | Result | Reference Ranges |
|------|--------|------------------|
| Cholesterol, serum | 206 | 75–200 |
| HDL | 51 | 30–70 |
| Triglycerides | 119 | 20–250 |

**Index: Organ or Disease-Oriented Panel, Lipid Panel**

**Code(s): 80061 Lipid panel**

## Case Study #9

| Test Name | Glycohemoglobin |
|---|---|
| Reference Range | 3.6–6.8 |
| Result | 5.9 |

Index: Glycohemoglobin

Code(s): 83036 Hemoglobin, glycosylated (A1C)

## Case Study #11

Urine Culture
Source: Straight catheter
Abundant Gram-positive cocci suggestive of streptococci
>100,000 CFU/ML Serratia Marcescens
>100,000 CFU/ML Enterococcus Species

Index: Culture, Bacteria, Urine

Code(s): 87086 Culture, bacterial; quantitative colony count, urine

## Exercise 6.2: Multiple Choice Questions

1. a

3. d

5. a

7. c

9. c

# Chapter 7

# Evaluation and Management Services

## Exercise 7.1: Case Studies

### Case Study #1

The patient was seen in the physician's office after falling and injuring her ankle. The physician performed a brief HPI, Review of Systems, a problem-focused exam, and the decision making was straightforward. What component(s) of the history is missing from this scenario?

**Answer: Personal, family, social history**

### Case Study #3

A 92-year-old new patient is seen in the patient's home to evaluate symptoms that include a cough and fever. The patient has a history of diabetes, and the family does not wish the patient to be hospitalized. A comprehensive history and examination with high-complexity decision making is performed. What is the correct E/M code assignment for this service?

**Answer: 99345 Home Visit E/M—For new patient with all 3 key components**

### Case Study #5

A patient is seen on January 23, 20XX by a primary care physician who is a member of University Associates. A cardiologist (also a member of University Associates) sees the patient on November 24 of the following year. Would the visit on November 24 be classified as a *new* or *established* patient?

**Answer: New. Even though the patient was seen one year prior, the patient is now seen by a physician of a different specialty, which would be classified as a new patient. CPT Evaluation and Management Services Guidelines defines a new patient as one who has not received any professional services from the physician/ qualified healthcare professional or another physician/qualified healthcare professional of the exact same specialty and subspecialty who belongs to the same group practice within the past three years.**

### Case Study #7

The physician sees a patient in Sunny Acres Nursing Facility as a follow-up visit. The patient has a urinary tract infection that is not responding to medication. The physician documents an expanded problem-focused interval history, a problem-focused examination, and the medical decision making was of moderate complexity. What is the correct CPT code assignment for this service?

**Answer: 99308 Subsequent Nursing Facility Care (Note that two of the three key components must be met or exceeded.)**

## Case Study #9

Physician documents that critical care services were provided to a 12-year-old patient for 45 minutes. What is the correct E/M code assignment for this service?

**Answer: 99291**

## Case Study #11

A 49-year-old established patient visits his family physician for a physical that is required by his place of employment. The physician documents a comprehensive history, performs an exam, and orders a series of routine tests, such as a chest X-ray and EKG. In addition, the physician counsels the patient about his smoking habit. What CPT code would be selected to represent this service?

**Answer: 99396 Preventive Medicine (40–64 years of age)**

## Exercise 7.2: Multiple Choice Questions

1. b
3. a
5. a
7. c
9. c

# Chapter 8

# Medicine

### Exercise 8.1: Case Studies

#### Case Study #1

A 55-year-old patient with Type II diabetes mellitus e-mails her registered dietitian to ask advice about adding a food product to her diet. The dietitian promptly responds to the question and keeps a record of this correspondence. The date of the last visit was two weeks ago.

> **Index: Online Internet Assessment and Management, Nonphysician**

> **Code(s): 98969 Online assessment and management service provided by qualified nonphysician healthcare professional to an established patient, guardian, or healthcare provider not originating from a related assessment and management service provided within the previous seven days, using the Internet or similar electronic communications network**

#### Case Study #3

A 25-year-old patient receives an IM injection of meningococcal serogroup B vaccine (MenB), 3-dose schedule.

> **Index: Immunization Administration, One Vaccine/Toxoid**
> **Vaccines, Meningococus, meningococcal, serogroup B (MenB)**

> **Code(s): 90471 Immunization administration, IM, one vaccine**
> **90621 Meningococcal recombinant lipoprotein vaccine, serogroup B (MenB), 3 dose schedule, for intramuscular use**

#### Case Study #5

A 45-year-old patient complains of sneezing, coughing, and occasional episodes of wheezing. The physician wants to determine the cause of these allergic symptoms and performs 30 percutaneous skin tests.

> **Index: Allergy Tests, Skin Tests, Allergen Extract**

> **Code(s): 95004 Percutaneous tests (Would need to specify the number of tests for claims processing.)**

#### Case Study #7

Photodynamic Therapy (PDT)
Patient was diagnosed with actinic keratosis with lesions on several locations of the face. The physician prepares a topical solution and applies photosensitizing agent in topical solution form to each lesion.

> **Index: Photodynamic Therapy, For Tissue Ablation**

> **Code(s): 96567 Photodynamic therapy**

## Case Study #9

A patient is seen in the Emergency Department with severe vomiting and diarrhea due to viral gastroenteritis. IV hydration is prescribed and takes one hour to administer.

**Index: Hydration, Intravenous**

**Code(s): 96360 Intravenous infusion, hydration; initial, 31 minutes to 1 hour**

## Case Study #11

A 67-year-old patient with multiple medical problems is currently taking six prescriptions and several over-the-counter agents. The primary care physician has a concern about side effects; therefore, the patient is referred to a pharmacist for assessment and management of medications. The pharmacist assesses the treatment and makes recommendations during the 10-minute face-to-face visit.

**Index: Medication Therapy Management, Pharmacist Provided**

**Code(s): 99605 Medication therapy management service(s) provided by a pharmacist, individual, face-to-face with patient, with assessment and intervention if provided; initial 15 minutes, new patient**

## Exercise 8.2: Multiple Choice Questions

1. b
3. d
5. a
7. c
9. d

# Chapter 9

# Anesthesia

## Exercise 9.1: Case Studies

### Case Study #1

This is a 49-year-old man with a chronic right-sided submandibular swelling over the last few years. The diagnosis of right sialoadenitis was made. An excision of right submandibular gland was performed.

**Index: Anesthesia, Salivary Gland**

**Code(s): 00100 Anesthesia for procedures on salivary glands, including biopsy**

### Case Study #3

Patient admitted for uterine fibroids and dysmenorrhea. The surgeon performs a vaginal hysterectomy.

**Index: Anesthesia, Hysterectomy, Vaginal**

**Code(s): 00944 Anesthesia, for vaginal procedures; vaginal hysterectomy**

### Case Study #5

The patient is a 65-year-old male who was recently treated for low anterior resection for a stage II superior rectal cancer. Adjuvant chemotherapy, planned. Placement of long-term venous access device was requested. Surgeon inserts a Port-a-Cath.

**Index: Anesthesia, Central Venous Circulation**

**Code(s): 00532 Anesthesia for access to central venous circulation**

### Case Study #7

Patient has a diagnosis of urinary retention. The surgeon performs a transurethral resection of the prostate.

**Index: Anesthesia, Transurethral Procedures, or Anesthesia, TURP**

**Code(s): 00914 Anesthesia for transurethral resection of prostate**

### Case Study #9

The patient is a 56-year-old male who presented to the ENT Clinic with a history of left-sided nasal obstruction. The following procedures were performed: left maxillary sinusotomy, left anterior ethmoidectomy, and removal of left nasal polyposis.

**Index: Anesthesia, Nose**

**Code(s): 00160 Anesthesia for procedures on nose and accessory sinuses; not otherwise specified**

## Exercise 9.2: Multiple Choice Questions

1. c
3. a
5. b
7. d
9. c

# Chapter 10

# HCPCS Level II

## Exercise 10.1: Case Studies

### Case Study #1

Foam dressing to cover a wound. Sterile pad, 20 sq in. without an adhesive border.

**Index: Foam Dressing**

**Code: A6210 Foam dressing, wound cover, sterile, pad size more than 16 sq. in. but less than or equal to 48 sq. in., without adhesive border, each dressing**

### Case Study #3

Patient has extreme dry eyes. Physician inserts temporary, absorbable lacrimal duct implants in each eye.

**Index: Lacrimal Duct Implant, Temporary**

**Code(s): A4262 × 2 Temporary, absorbable lacrimal duct implant, each**

### Case Study #5

Floating kyphosis pad

**Index: Kyphosis Pad**

**Code: L1025 Kyphosis pad, floating**

### Case Study #7

Portable paraffin bath unit

**Index: Paraffin Bath Unit**

**Code: E0235 Paraffin bath unit, portable**

### Case Study #9

IV pole for infusion

**Index: IV Pole**

**Code(s): E0776 IV pole**

### Case Study #11

EMG biofeedback device

**Index: EMG**

**Code(s): E0746 Electromyography (EMG), biofeedback device**

## Case Study #13

Home blood glucose monitor

**Index: Monitor, Blood Glucose**

**Code: E0607 Blood glucose home monitor**

## Case Study #15

Ostomy belt

**Index: Belt, Ostomy**

**Code(s): A4367 Ostomy belt, each**

## Case Study #17

PAP smear (two smears) performed by technician under the supervision of a physician

**Index: Laboratory Test, Toxicology**

**Code: P3000 Screening papanicolaou smear, cervical or vaginal, up to three smears, by technician under physician supervision**

## Case Study #19

Voice amplifier

**Index: Voice Amplifier**

**Code: L8510 Voice amplifier**

## Exercise 10.2: Multiple Choice Coding

1. b

3. d

5. c

7. d

9. d

# Chapter 11

# Reimbursement in the Ambulatory Setting

## Exercise 11.1: Crossword Puzzle

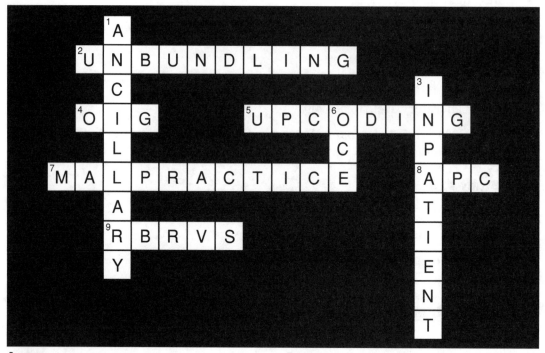

### Across

2. Incorrectly assigning multiple codes [UNBUNDLING]
4. Develops yearly workplan [OIG]
5. Assigning a code for higher payment [UPCODING]
7. RVU's include physician work, practice, and _____ expenses [MALPRACTICE]
8. Reimbursement system for ambulatory surgery centers [APC]
9. Reimbursement system for physicians [RBRVS]

### Down

1. Status indicator X identifies _____ services [ANCILLARY]
3. Status indicator C describes _____ procedures [INPATIENT]
6. Tool used to weed out incorrect claims [OCE]

## Exercise 11.2:

### Exercise #1—Medical Necessity

A 47-year-old female patient is seen in an outpatient setting for a variety of symptoms, including fatigue, weakness, and insomnia. The physician orders the following tests:

```
FBS
PSA
WBC
T3, T4
TSH
```

Which test(s) does not meet medical necessity?

**Answer: PSA (Prostate-Specific Antigen) would not be appropriate for a female patient.**

### Exercise #3—Medical Necessity

Which of the following diagnoses would support CPT code 51726 Complex cystometrogram?
**(c) Stress incontinence**

### Exercise #5—Medical Necessity

Which of the following diagnoses would be linked appropriately to CPT code 11640, Excision malignant lesion?
**(b) Melanoma of the forehead**

### Exercise #7—Editing Codes

Which of the following codes would not be appropriate for a female patient?
**(a) Mastectomy for gynecomastia (swelling of breast tissue in males)**